42/=

RECOMMENDED METHODS FOR THE ANALYSIS OF TRADE EFFLUENTS

Recommended Methods for the Analysis of Trade Effluents

Prepared by

A JOINT COMMITTEE OF

THE ASSOCIATION OF BRITISH CHEMICAL MANUFACTURERS

and

THE SOCIETY FOR ANALYTICAL CHEMISTRY

Published for

THE SOCIETY FOR ANALYTICAL CHEMISTRY

by

W. HEFFER & SONS LTD.

1958

Printed in Great Britain at the Works of
W. HEFFER & SONS LTD., CAMBRIDGE, ENGLAND

FOREWORD

The scope of this work is so clearly set out by Mr. H. N. Wilson in his Preface that a Foreword is scarcely necessary.

Reference must, however, be made to the rapidity with which this lengthy and exacting task has been accomplished, and I think it is fair to say that without the help of the Secretariat of the Analytical Methods Committee of the Society for Analytical Chemistry in the very arduous task of drafting the methods, this work could not have been completed in the short time of three years. It is therefore appropriate that we should acknowledge the financial assistance which has been received from the Society for Analytical Chemistry Analytical Methods Trust Fund, established by donations from Industry for the maintenance of the Secretariat.

Our thanks are also due to the Trust Fund for a grant towards the expenses of an investigation which was found to be necessary to devise a method for the detection of silver in effluents in the very low concentrations at which silver toxicity becomes a serious problem. This investigation has now been successfully completed and the method will be published shortly.

In conclusion, it is a pleasure to acknowledge the enthusiastic and valuable support which has been given by all members of the various panels concerned in this work.

J. H. HAMENCE,
President.
THE SOCIETY FOR ANALYTICAL CHEMISTRY.

24*th July*, 1958.

Contents

Preface

IT has long been admitted that neither the methods devised for the analysis of sewage and sewage-works effluents nor the methods commonly used for the analysis of potable waters are always applicable to the examination of trade effluents. Indeed, no standard or generally recognised handbook or compilation of methods dealing with this subject has been published in this country. The number of possible contaminants is very large; that some of them will interfere with the "standard" methods is obvious, but no attempt has yet been made in Great Britain to collect together the most reliable information on the subject, and analysts concerned with such analyses have had to exercise their experience in improvising methods suitable for the effluents under examination.

This position has been rather unsatisfactory for some years; the analysis of samples was lengthened and made more expensive, and there was always the possibility of dispute arising on the actual composition of effluents. The passing of the Rivers (Prevention of Pollution) Act in 1951 threw into strong relief the undesirable features of the position; its provisions will necessitate more analyses being carried out than previously, and it is very desirable that the parties concerned should as far as possible use the same methods.

The lack of any "standard" or accepted methods of analysis was recognised by the Federation of British Industries Technical Legislation Committee, which asked the Association of British Chemical Manufacturers to investigate the position; so, in February, 1953, the A.B.C.M. Trade Effluents Committee, as a first step, set up an Analytical Sub-Committee. This Sub-Committee of eight members was drawn from diverse branches of the chemical industry and was widely representative of analytical experience within the Association. It was directed to "assist the Trade Effluents Committee" and its primary task was to "approve or devise suitable analytical methods for trade effluents." During the course of the work, it became clear that the codification of suitable modifications of the non-specific tests was most difficult. These tests are more used in non-industrial than in industrial laboratories, and it was thought that the Sub-Committee would be much helped by close collaboration with non-industrial experts. The A.B.C.M. Council gave its approval to an approach to The Society for Analytical Chemistry, and a meeting of representatives of the two bodies was held on February 10th, 1954.

At that meeting it was agreed that a Joint A.B.C.M. - S.A.C. Committee on Methods for the Analysis of Trade Effluents should be formed. Its terms of reference were "to devise and recommend methods of analysis as applied to trade effluents, specifying in each case their applicability and limitations, but not the interpretation of the results of such tests as would be used to decide on the quality of an effluent."

It was expected "that the Joint Committee would work through specialist panels. Such methods, on approval by the Council of the S.A.C., would be published by the Society as Recommended Methods of the Joint Committee, with possible reprints in suitable form for individual sale. The urgency of the need for early publication was noted. . . ." The Joint Committee held its first meeting on March 19th, 1954, and set up four panels to deal with various types of test.

The Joint Committee's task was to find methods that are not only capable of determining toxic constituents with sufficient accuracy in the very small amounts that have been found to cause damage to the animal and vegetable life of rivers, etc., but are at the same time practical and quick enough to be used in the rapidly changing conditions that may prevail. The first intention of the Joint Committee was to make a literature search and to recommend the best method available for each particular impurity. Unfortunately, the literature on the analysis of trade effluents is scant and it soon became obvious that for a number of methods experimental work would be necessary. In view of Industry's need for recommended methods, the tests were published individually in *The Analyst* as soon as they were deemed satisfactory. At the same time, results of some of the supporting experimental work carried out were also published independently by panel members.

Account has been taken of the "Methods of Chemical Analysis as Applied to Sewage and Sewage Effluents" (Second Edition, 1956) published by H.M. Stationery Office for the Ministry of Housing and Local Government; the avoidance of conflict with these methods is particularly important in the determination of oxygen demand and, for this reason, permission was obtained for reproduction in full of the methods for the determination of biochemical oxygen demand and of dissolved oxygen, although it has, of course, been necessary to make modifications to cover special requirements for trade effluents. In addition, a section has been included on the manometric technique and its advantages in the determination of the biochemical oxygen demand of trade effluents.

As far as possible the methods selected or devised are generally applicable over a wide range of contents, but for some constituents it has been necessary to give modified, or different, methods for application to lower parts of the range and the lack of specificity of reagents for some of the metallic constituents has caused difficulty when very small amounts have to be determined. In some circumstances any method may require modification, and in material as variable as industrial effluents it is almost inevitable that from time to time there will be components present that will interfere with the recommended tests. Even so, the recommended methods should be serviceable in the vast majority of cases. Limitations known to the Joint Committee have been indicated, and the Joint Committee ventures to hope that analysts who discover others will communicate with the Secretary of the Analytical Methods Committee of the S.A.C., so that a second edition may be more informative.

In conclusion, the Joint Committee wishes to thank the many individuals, firms and organisations who have made their experience available. In particular, it wishes to acknowledge the very courteous actions of the American Public Health Association and of the Ministry of Housing and Local Government, both of whom provided complete sets of proofs of their "Standard Methods for the Examination of Water, Sewage, and Industrial Wastes" (Tenth Edition) and "Methods of Chemical Analysis as Applied to Sewage and Sewage Effluents" (Second Edition), respectively, many months in advance of publication.

H. N. WILSON.

Chairman, A.B.C.M. - S.A.C. Joint Committee on
Methods for the Analysis of Trade Effluents.

Constitution of Committees

A.B.C.M. TRADE EFFLUENTS COMMITTEE—ANALYTICAL SUB-COMMITTEE

H. N. Wilson, F.R.I.C. (*Chairman*)	Imperial Chemical Industries Ltd. (Billingham Division)
D. C. Garratt, Ph.D., D.Sc., F.R.I.C. (*Secretary*)	Boots Pure Drug Co. Ltd.
F. G. Broughall, B.Sc., F.R.I.C.	Midland Tar Distillers Ltd.
C. L. Evans, M.Inst.F., M.Inst.GasE., F.R.I.C.	Brotherton & Co. Ltd.
J. G. Maltby, B.Sc., F.R.I.C.	Distillers Co. Ltd.
T. B. Moore, B.Sc.	North Thames Gas Board
I. S. Wilson, M.Sc., Ph.D., A.R.I.C.	Monsanto Chemicals Ltd.
C. Lea	Imperial Chemical Industries Ltd.

A.B.C.M.—S.A.C. JOINT COMMITTEE

Main Committee—

Representing the Association of British Chemical Manufacturers—

H. N. Wilson, F.R.I.C. (*Chairman*)	Imperial Chemical Industries Ltd. (Billingham Division)
J. G. Maltby, B.Sc., F.R.I.C. (*Secretary*)	Distillers Co. Ltd.
F. G. Broughall, B.Sc., F.R.I.C.	Midland Tar Distillers Ltd.
D. C. Garratt, Ph.D., D.Sc., F.R.I.C.	Boots Pure Drug Co. Ltd.
I. S. Wilson, M.Sc., Ph.D., A.R.I.C.	Monsanto Chemicals Ltd.

Representing the Society for Analytical Chemistry—

J. H. Hamence, M.Sc., Ph.D., F.R.I.C.	Public Analyst, Official Agricultural Analyst and Consulting Chemist
L. Klein, M.Sc., Ph.D., M.Inst.S.P., F.R.I.C.	Mersey River Board
C. J. Regan, B.Sc., F.R.I.C.	*formerly* Chemist-in-Chief, London County Council
J. G. Sherratt, B.Sc., F.R.I.C.	Public Analyst and Consulting Analytical Chemist
N. T. Wilkinson, F.R.I.C.	Imperial Chemical Industries Ltd. (Alkali Division)
K. A. Williams, B.Sc., Ph.D., A.Inst.P., M.Inst.Pet., F.R.I.C.	Analytical and Consulting Chemist

---

J. S. Evans	*formerly* Federation of British Industries
Miss C. H. Tinker, B.Sc., Ph.D., A.R.I.C.	Secretary to the Analytical Methods Committee of the S.A.C. (*co-opted*)

PUBLICATIONS SUB-COMMITTEE—
 H. N. WILSON
   (*Chairman*)
 J. G. MALTBY
   (*Secretary*)
 J. B. ATTRILL, M.A., F.R.I.C.   Editor of *The Analyst*
 J. H. HAMENCE
 Miss C. H. TINKER

PANEL 1: ORGANIC MATTER—GENERAL—
 C. J. REGAN
   (*Chairman*)
 G. S. CLEMENTS, A.R.C.S., F.R.I.C.   Public Health Department, London
   (*Secretary*)   County Council
 W. M. CAMERON, M.Inst.S.P., F.R.I.C. Main Drainage Department, Middle-
                                    sex County Council
 W. T. LOCKETT, M.Sc.   *formerly* Main Drainage Department,
                                    Middlesex County Council
 T. B. MOORE, B.Sc.   North Thames Gas Board
 A. E. J. PETTET, B.A.   D.S.I.R., Water Pollution Research
                                    Laboratory
 I. S. WILSON
 Miss C. H. TINKER

PANEL 2: METALLIC CONTAMINANTS—
 N. T. WILKINSON
   (*Chairman*)
 Miss C. H. TINKER
   (*Secretary*)
 R. BELCHER, Ph.D., D.Sc., F.Inst.F., University of Birmingham (Depart-
   F.R.I.C.   ment of Chemistry)
 D. C. GARRATT
 J. H. HAMENCE
 J. G. SHERRATT

PANEL 3: NON-METALLIC CONTAMINANTS—
 F. G. BROUGHALL
   (*Chairman*)
 Miss C. H. TINKER
   (*Secretary*)
 W. G. CAREY, F.R.I.C.   Public Analyst and Official Agricul-
                               tural Analyst; Consultant
 G. U. HOUGHTON, M.Sc., Ph.D.,   South Essex Waterworks Co.
   F.R.I.C.
 E. A. W. WHITLOCK, B.Sc., A.R.I.C. Wallace & Tiernan Ltd.
   Deputy: J. F. MALPAS, B.Sc.,
   A.R.I.C.

PANEL 4: PHYSICAL METHODS—
 J. G. SHERRATT
   (*Chairman*)
 Miss C. H. TINKER
   (*Secretary*)
 L. KLEIN
 G. A. VAUGHAN, F.R.I.C.   Coal Tar Research Association
 K. A. WILLIAMS

Sampling

Information to be recorded at the time of sampling should include—

details of type of sample,
the place and time of sampling,
the temperature of sample, and
any other relevant data.

Industrial effluents often vary so rapidly and so widely in character that "snap" samples may not afford a reliable guide to the nature of the over-all discharge. In such instances a suitable number of individual samples should be taken at appropriate intervals and made into a composite sample. When practicable, the volumes of the individual samples should be related to the volume of effluent flowing at the time.

In certain circumstances it may be more convenient for a composite sample to be prepared by the analyst, who, for this purpose, will require a record of the approximate flow of effluent at the time each individual sample was taken.

Some effluents are of such a heterogeneous character that general directions for sampling cannot be given. The precise technique to be adopted in such instances should be agreed between the analyst and the other parties concerned.

Although the amount of sample to be taken should be agreed with the analyst, at least 2 litres will usually be required for a complete range of tests. The sample should be contained in a clean glass bottle with a ground stopper. Wide-mouthed bottles kept specially for the purpose are required when sampling oily liquids. New bottles should be washed with acid and thoroughly rinsed with distilled water before being brought into use.

For certain tests special samples will be required, and these should be taken as described later.

SPECIAL CONSIDERATIONS

UNSTABLE EFFLUENTS—

When effluents contain dissolved gases, readily oxidisable substances or other substances that may disappear during transit, special precautions may be necessary, e.g., samples intended for the determination of dissolved oxygen should be taken with an under-water sampling device such as the Casella apparatus,* or the apparatus described in "Standard Methods for the Examination of Water, Sewage and Industrial Wastes," Tenth Edition (p. 251), published by the American Public Health Association Inc.; samples in which traces of sulphide are to be determined should be analysed without delay or treated immediately with a suitable fixative, e.g., zinc acetate.

EFFLUENTS CONTAINING IMMISCIBLE LIQUIDS—

The proportionate ratio of two immiscible liquids of different specific gravities (e.g., mineral oil and water) usually cannot be maintained in a sample obtained by dipping a jug or other container into an effluent that is flowing in or from a pipe. The most satisfactory method of sampling two-phase liquids is to use a sampling tube that is capable of withdrawing a complete section of the effluent as it flows in a rectangular culvert or trough: in most instances, however, effluents will have

* Obtainable from Messrs. C. F. Casella & Co. Ltd., Regent House, Fitzroy Square, London, W.1.

to be sampled from the outfall of a pipe or from a stream and in these circumstances some of the effluent should first be collected in a large cylindrical vessel having a capacity of two to three gallons.   A sectional sampling tube should be used to

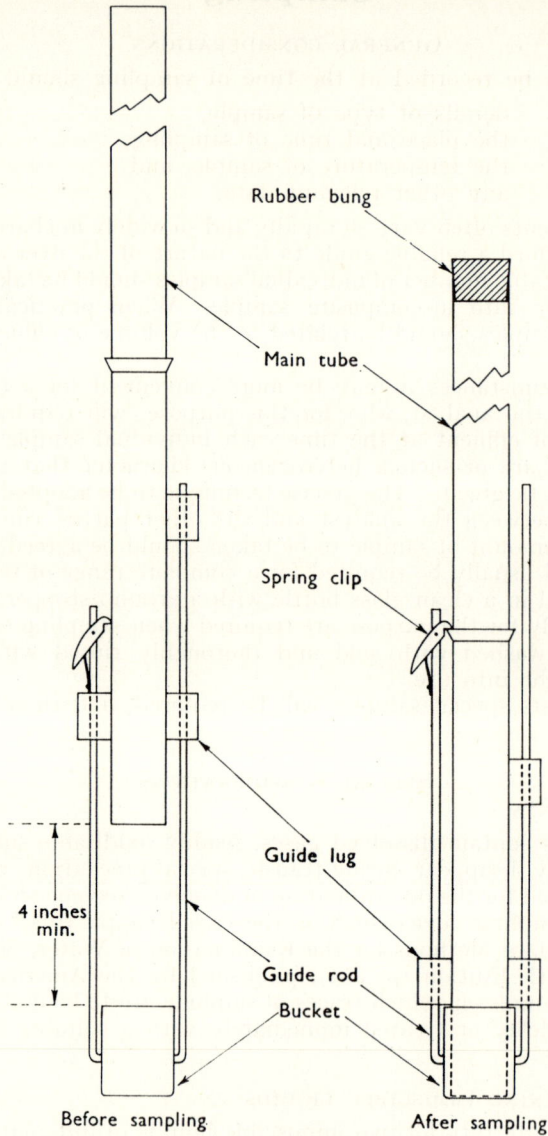

Fig. 1.   Sampling tube

withdraw the test sample from this.   A sampling tube suitable for sampling effluents that do not contain highly viscous matter (*e.g.*, tar) is described below (see Fig. 1); the measurements are approximate.

The sampler consists of a heavy-gauge brass tube, 3 feet long, with an outside diameter of 1½ inches.   Over one end of the tube is fitted a brass bucket made from a piece of tube 2 inches long and sealed at one end. The bucket has an internal diameter $\frac{1}{16}$ inch greater than the outside diameter of the main tube. To opposite sides of the bucket are brazed two brass rods, $\frac{1}{4}$ inch in diameter, which pass through guides brazed to the sides of the main tube. The rods are so arranged that the top of the bucket can be withdrawn to a distance of not less than 4 inches from the bottom of the main tube, and they guide the bucket into a position covering the end of the tube when it is pushed back again. A suitable spring catch is provided on one of the guide rods so that the bucket is automatically locked into the top position when it is raised to its highest point. The open end of the sampling tube is fitted with a rubber bung.

To take a sectional sample, the spring catch is released and the bucket is drawn as far as possible away from the end of the main tube. The rubber bung is withdrawn from the other end. The tube is lowered vertically through the liquid to be sampled until the bottom of the bucket rests on the bottom of the culvert or of the vessel that has been filled with the effluent. The main tube is then pushed down, guided by the brass rods, to the limit of its travel, whereupon the spring catch locks the bucket in the raised position covering the end of the tube. The rubber bung is tightly inserted in the open end and the tube is withdrawn. The outside of the sampler is wiped free from adhering liquid, the bucket and the lower part of the tube are inserted into a wide-mouthed bottle of suitable capacity, and the rubber bung is removed. The sample section of the liquid will flow into the bottle, leaving a small quantity of liquid in the bucket. The tube is then tilted so that this liquid is added to the main bulk of the sample. The operation is repeated until a sufficient quantity has been collected. At least 1 inch of air space should be left between the top level of the liquid and the stopper of the bottle.

Preliminary Examination of the Sample

General Description

The analyst should record his observations on the general appearance of the sample, particularly noting any tendency to foam, its colour and odour, and the presence of visible oil, tar or other floating, suspended or settled matter. Any change that is observed in the appearance of the sample should be recorded.

Colour

Trade effluents may vary so widely that the usual methods for determining colour in potable waters may not be applicable. When a quantitative figure is required, it may be obtained with the Lovibond Tintometer or other comparable instrument if the effluent is not turbid, but in most instances the analyst's observation of colour included in the general description of the sample will be sufficient.

Temperature

Record the temperature of the effluent at the time of sampling to the nearest $0.5°$ C.

pH Value

The pH value of an effluent may be determined either electrometrically or colorimetrically. The colorimetric method is convenient and sufficiently accurate for general work when the sample is relatively free from colour and turbidity.

ELECTROMETRIC METHOD

APPARATUS—

Any reliable commercial instrument with a glass electrode may be used; it should be standardised by one or both of the buffer solutions specified below.

Standard buffer solution of pH 4—Dissolve 10.21 g of anhydrous potassium hydrogen phthalate, $COOH \cdot C_6H_4 \cdot COOK$, in boiled and cooled distilled water and dilute the solution to 1 litre.

Standard buffer solution of pH 9—Dissolve 19.07 g of borax, $Na_2B_4O_7.10H_2O$, in boiled and cooled distilled water and dilute the solution to 1 litre.

The pH of these buffer solutions varies with temperature in accordance with the following table—

		True pH at temperature, ° C, of								
Buffer of	5	10	15	20	25	30	35	40	45	50
pH 4 ..	4·01	4·00	4·00	4·00	4·01	4·01	4·02	4·03	4·04	4·06
pH 9 ..	9·38	9·33	9·27	9·22	9·18	9·14	9·10	9·07	9·04	9·01

It should be noted that the glass-electrode instrument cannot be used directly on oily or greasy effluents, but an approximate value for the pH can be obtained if these are first filtered to remove the oil or grease.

Special glass electrodes are necessary for alkaline liquids of pH greater than 9. The precautions recommended by the makers of the instrument should be observed.

COLORIMETRIC METHOD

REAGENTS—

The indicators most generally used for the colorimetric determination of pH values of effluents are listed in Table I.

TABLE I

INDICATORS FOR USE IN THE COLORIMETRIC DETERMINATION OF pH VALUES OF EFFLUENTS

Indicator	pH range	Volume of 0·1 N sodium hydroxide required per 0·1 g of indicator, ml
Thymol blue (acid range)	1·2 to 2·8	2·15
Bromophenol blue	2·8 to 4·6	1·5
Bromocresol green	3·6 to 5·2	1·45
Chlorophenol red	4·8 to 6·4	3·15
Bromothymol blue	6·0 to 7·6	1·6
Phenol red	6·8 to 8·4	2·85
Cresol red	7·2 to 8·8	2·65
Thymol blue (alkali range)	8·0 to 9·6	2·15
Phenolphthalein	8·2 to 10·0	—
Thymolphthalein	9·3 to 10·5	—
Thymol violet	9·0 to 12·0	—

To prepare the indicator solutions, moisten 0·1 g of the solid indicator with about 2 ml of ethanol (or industrial methylated spirit) in a glass mortar, triturate with the amount of 0·1 N sodium hydroxide shown in the third column of Table I and dilute with distilled water to 25 ml. Dilute this stock solution with 20 per cent. ethanol (or industrial methylated spirit) to make a 0·04 per cent. solution and adjust the pH to approximately the mid-point of the range by the addition of approximately 0·02 N acid or alkali, freshly prepared.

Phenolphthalein, thymolphthalein and thymol violet are used in 0·1 per cent. solution in 95 per cent. ethanol (or industrial methylated spirit) and any acidity in the alcohol should be neutralised with alkali after the indicator solution has been prepared.

All indicators should be stored in resistance-glass containers with ground stoppers; corks should not be used.

PROCEDURE—

First determine the approximate pH value of the sample by means of a universal indicator and then select the appropriate indicator, avoiding extremes of the range. Transfer by pipette 0·4 ml of the indicator solution into a clean test-tube of colourless glass, kept specially for the purpose, and add from a pipette 10 ml of the sample (avoid agitation), mixing gently with the pipette. Compare with buffer tubes of different pH values prepared with this indicator. Directions for the preparation of buffer solutions covering the range pH 1·5 to 11 are given in "Thorpe's Dictionary of Applied Chemistry," Fourth Edition, Volume 2, p. 122, and in other standard works.

If the sample is coloured, compensate for its colour by using a comparator in which an extra tube of 10 ml of the sample, without indicator, can be viewed with the buffer tube.

NOTES—1. Alternatively, commercial instruments that are available for the colorimetric determination of pH may be used, provided that the maker's instructions are followed.

2. In water containing residual free chlorine, the colour of the indicator may be affected and the colorimetric method is not applicable.

B

Transparency

PRINCIPLE OF METHOD—

The depth of liquid at which a standard mark is just obscured is taken to be a measure of the transparency.

APPARATUS—

A colourless glass tube, 620 $\pm$ 10 mm long and of internal diameter 25 $\pm$ 1 mm, fitted with a plane glass bottom and graduated in millimetres from the bottom to a height of 50 mm and at every 5 mm from 50 mm to 600 mm. This tube is fitted with a side tube, 6 to 7 mm in diameter, at a height of about 50 mm from the bottom, connected by rubber tubing to a glass reservoir, having a capacity of 300 ml. A black cross with lines 1 mm wide on white paper is pasted on the outside of the bottom of the glass tube so that the cross can be observed down the tube.

PROCEDURE—

Support the tube vertically, preferably illuminated by north daylight. Pour in the liquid slowly, observing the depth of liquid at which the black cross just disappears. If this depth is greater than the height of the side arm, variation of depth can most easily be attained by suitable manipulation of the reservoir.

Report the transparency as the depth of the column in millimetres through which the cross is just not visible.

NOTES—1. Observations may be made on the sample after a suitable period of settlement or on the sample when uniformly mixed.

2. The determination of transparency cannot be made with great precision; it should be noted that the transparency may vary considerably with the time that has elapsed since the sample was taken.

Settleable Solids

The amount of settleable solids is defined as the weight in milligrams per litre of insoluble matter that will settle from an effluent under prescribed conditions. It is often convenient to specify a period of 4 hours for settlement, but the appropriate time will vary with the purpose for which the information is desired, and it must be left to the discretion of the analyst, who should report the settling time adopted.

PROCEDURE—

Fill a 100-ml Nessler cylinder to the upper mark with the well mixed sample. Allow the sample to stand undisturbed at a temperature between 10° and 15° C for the specified time. Without disturbing the sediment, withdraw the top 50 ml and determine the amount of suspended solids in the separated liquid by the method prescribed for "Total Suspended Solids." Calculate the results in milligrams per litre and deduct this figure from that found for total suspended solids. The difference between the two values is recorded as "settleable solids."

Total Suspended Solids

Samples containing an excessive amount of suspended matter, and those containing colloidal matter, are often difficult to filter. When it is impracticable to use the filtration method, the centrifugal method should be used.

NOTE—If the suspended matter includes volatile oils, the following procedures only measure the non-volatile part. The centrifugal method is not applicable if any part of the suspended matter floats.

FILTRATION METHOD

PRINCIPLE OF METHOD—

Suspended matter is determined by weighing the residue after filtering the effluent through an asbestos pad in a Gooch crucible.

REAGENT—

Asbestos cream—Prepare a cream with distilled water by adding 15 g of acid-washed medium-fibre asbestos (prepared specially for use with Gooch crucibles) to 1 litre of distilled water. Some asbestos supplied for this purpose contains too much fine asbestos powder; this fine material should be removed by repeated decantations.

PROCEDURE—

Prepare an asbestos fibre pad in a 30-ml Gooch crucible by adding sufficient of the asbestos cream to produce a pad 3 mm thick and containing about 0·3 g dry weight of asbestos. Wash the pad with distilled water, dry the whole at 100° to 105° C for 1 hour, cool and weigh. If mineral suspended solids are subsequently to be determined, the crucible and pad must first be ignited at 500° C and cooled before weighing.

It is desirable to use the maximum volume of the well mixed sample that can be passed through the crucible without clogging the filter-pad. Filter successive increments of 10 ml of the well shaken sample, using gentle suction, and add each increment just before the pad becomes dry; continue until the rate of filtration becomes inconveniently slow, or until about 200 ml of the sample have been used. If a pipette is used for measuring the increments, the orifice should be wide enough to prevent it becoming clogged during the operation. Carefully wash the pad with 5 ml of distilled water, dry the whole at 100° to 105° C and weigh. Express the result as milligrams of suspended solids per litre of sample.

If a measurement of the dissolved solids is required, retain the filtrate.

If a determination of the mineral suspended solids is required, ignite the crucible in a muffle furnace at a temperature not exceeding 500° C for 15 minutes, cool and re-weigh.

CENTRIFUGAL METHOD

APPARATUS—

Centrifuge.
Cone-shaped centrifuge tubes, having capacities of 50 ml.

PROCEDURE—

Transfer 50 ml of the well mixed sample to a centrifuge tube, balance it in the usual way and centrifuge the liquid for not less than 5 minutes at a relative centrifugal force of 1400 to 3000.* Decant the supernatant liquid, refill the tube with distilled water to the mark and centrifuge again for a further period of 5 minutes. Again decant the supernatant liquid and transfer the sediment with the aid of a wash-bottle to a weighed silica, porcelain or platinum dish. Dry the residue at 100° to 105° C for 1 hour and weigh. Express the result as milligrams of suspended solids per litre of sample.

If a measurement of the dissolved solids is required, retain the clear decanted liquid and washings.

* The relative centrifugal force
$$= 1·12 \times 10^{-5} \times rN^2,$$
where $r =$ the radius in centimetres from the centre of the head of the centrifuge to the closed end (bottom) of the tube when in rotation, and
$N =$ the number of revolutions per minute.

If desired, the residue can be ignited, as in the filtration method, to determine the mineral suspended matter.

Residue on Evaporation

The residue on evaporation is the total solid matter obtained under the prescribed conditions.

Note—In the presence of substantial quantities of hygroscopic substances, *e.g.*, calcium chloride, an accurate result cannot be obtained by this method.

PROCEDURE—

Evaporate on a water bath 100 ml of the well mixed sample in a previously heated and weighed basin. Dry the residue at 100° to 105° C in an oven for 1 hour, cover the basin with a clock-glass, cool in a desiccator and re-weigh the basin. Express the result as milligrams of residue per litre of sample.

Dissolved Solids

The dissolved solids may be calculated indirectly as the difference between the residue on evaporation and the total suspended solids. However, if the dissolved-solids content in the effluent is low and the suspended-solids content is high, a direct determination is necessary. It is preferable to adopt the centrifugal method of separating suspended matter in order that a sufficiently large volume of separated liquid shall be available for this determination.

PROCEDURE—

Transfer quantitatively to a previously weighed basin the clear liquid from which the suspended solids have been separated by filtering or centrifuging. Evaporate it to dryness on a water bath. Dry the residue at 100° to 105° C in an oven for 1 hour, cover the basin with a clock-glass, cool in a desiccator and re-weigh the basin. Express the result as milligrams of dissolved solids per litre of sample.

Acidity

DEFINITION—

Titratable acidity is defined as the number of millilitres of $0\cdot1$ N alkali that are required to raise the pH of a litre of an acid effluent to 4.

APPLICABILITY—

Acidity as defined is assumed to be mineral acidity because organic acids are not likely to be present in sufficient concentration to reduce the pH below $4\cdot0$.

A titration to the phenolphthalein end-point (sometimes described as "total acidity") may be made, but the result is often difficult to interpret; among substances that cause difficulty are salts of strong acids and weak bases, and carbon dioxide. If a determination of organic acid is required, a method must be devised to suit the circumstances, *e.g.*, steam-distillation of volatile acids, or extraction of non-volatile acids from the dry residue with a suitable solvent.

REAGENTS—

Methyl orange indicator solution—A $0\cdot04$ per cent. solution in 20 per cent. ethanol.

or

Screened methyl orange indicator solution—Dissolve 1 g of methyl orange and $1\cdot4$ g of xylene-cyanol FF in 500 ml of ethanol.

or

Bromophenol blue indicator solution—A $0\cdot04$ per cent. solution in 20 per cent. ethanol.

Sodium hydroxide solution, $0\cdot1$ N.

PROCEDURE—

Colourless (*or nearly colourless*) *effluents*—Remove any suspended matter from the sample by filtration or centrifuging, and transfer 100 ml of the clear liquid by pipette into a 750-ml conical flask. Add 5 drops of one of the indicator solutions and dilute the solution with 400 ml of freshly boiled and cooled distilled water.

NOTE—If the colour of the indicator is bleached, repeat the determination, adding a crystal or two of sodium thiosulphate before the addition of the indicator.

Titrate with 0·1 N sodium hydroxide solution, and express the result as the number of millilitres of 0·1 N alkali per litre of sample.

If the titration exceeds 30 ml of 0·1 N alkali, use a smaller quantity of sample.

Deeply coloured effluents—If the colour of the effluent diluted as described above interferes with the determination of the end-point, an electrometric titration must be used.

Alkalinity

DEFINITION—

Titratable alkalinity is defined as the number of millilitres of 0·1 N acid required to lower the pH of a litre of an alkaline effluent to 8 ("phenolphthalein alkalinity") or to 4 ("methyl orange alkalinity").

REAGENTS—

Methyl orange indicator solution—A 0·04 per cent. solution in 20 per cent. ethanol.

or

Screened methyl orange indicator solution—Dissolve 1 g of methyl orange and 1·4 g of xylene-cyanol FF in 500 ml of ethanol.

or

Bromophenol blue indicator solution—A 0·04 per cent. solution in 20 per cent. ethanol.

Phenolphthalein indicator solution—A 0·1 per cent. solution in 50 per cent. ethanol.

Hydrochloric acid solution, 0·1 N.

PROCEDURE—

Colourless or nearly colourless effluents—Remove any suspended matter from the sample by filtration or centrifuging, and transfer 100 ml of the clear liquid by pipette into a 750-ml flask, add 1 ml of phenolphthalein indicator solution and titrate with 0·1 N hydrochloric acid to the end-point of this indicator. Express the result as the number of millilitres of 0·1 N acid per litre of sample (*i.e.*, "phenolphthalein alkalinity").

To the solution neutralised to phenolphthalein add 5 drops of either solution of the methyl orange indicator or of bromophenol blue and continue the titration to the end-point. Express the sum of the two titrations in terms of millilitres of 0·1 N acid per litre of sample (*i.e.*, "methyl orange alkalinity").

Deeply coloured effluents—If the colour of the effluent interferes with the titration, and the interference cannot be overcome by suitable dilution with freshly boiled and cooled distilled water, an electrometric titration must be used.

NOTE—Some effluents may contain insoluble alkalinity in the form of calcium carbonate or calcium hydroxide or both. For these, the total alkalinity is determined on the unfiltered sample by adding an excess of 0·1 N hydrochloric acid, boiling off the carbon dioxide, cooling and titrating back to the phenolphthalein end-point with 0·1 N alkali.

Hardness

The commonly used methods for determining total hardness that depend upon titration with disodium ethylenediaminetetra-acetate (EDTA) cannot be used for all effluents.   If, however, the only cations present are calcium, magnesium and the alkali metals, the recommended method for determining calcium and magnesium may be used for the determination of total hardness.

Two methods are described.   Method A gives accurate results for total hardness in terms of the definition below, but it involves a lengthy procedure unless a flame photometer is available.   Method B may be used when extreme accuracy is not required.

DEFINITIONS—

Total hardness is defined as the sum of all the metallic cations, except those of the alkali metals, calculated in terms of calcium carbonate.

Carbonate (temporary) hardness is defined as that part of the hardness attributable to the bicarbonates of the same cations.   Usually, the carbonate hardness is the same as the "methyl orange alkalinity," but this is not so when the effluent also contains the bicarbonates, carbonates or hydroxides of the alkali or alkaline-earth metals.

METHOD A

PRINCIPLE OF METHOD—

The method consists in determining the total cationic strength by ion exchange, followed by determination of the alkali-metal cations.   The difference between the results of the two determinations calculated in terms of calcium carbonate is the total hardness.

APPARATUS—

Chromatographic column, consisting of a glass tube 25 cm long with an approximate outside diameter of 1·75 cm, drawn out at its lower end.   The upper end should have an open bulb of approximately 100 ml capacity fused to it.

Pack a small quantity of cotton-wool in the constricted end of the tube.   Pour in 20 g of Zeo-Karb 225 ion-exchange resin and tap the tube gently to consolidate the resin.   Place a small piece of cotton-wool at the top of the resin column.

Activate the resin by passing 1 litre of approximately $2 N$ hydrochloric acid through it, followed by distilled water, until the eluate is free from chloride ion. When the level of the distilled water is about 1 inch above the resin bed, place a stopper in the bulb and allow the column to remain wet until it is required.

REAGENTS—

Sodium hydroxide solution, 0·02 N.

Hydrochloric acid, sp.gr. 1·18.

Barium hydroxide.

Ammonium hydroxide, sp.gr. 0·880.

Ammonium carbonate solution, 5 per cent. w/v.

Indicator solution A—Dissolve 0·125 g of methyl red in 50 ml of 95 per cent. ethanol (or industrial methylated spirit).

Indicator solution B—Dissolve 0·083 g of methylene blue in 50 ml of 95 per cent. ethanol (or industrial methylated spirit).

NOTE—As these indicator solutions, if mixed, deteriorate on storage, they are added separately during the procedure.

Phenolphthalein indicator solution—A 0·1 per cent. solution in 95 per cent. ethanol (or industrial methylated spirit).

PROCEDURE FOR DETERMINING TOTAL CATIONS—

Evaporate 200 ml, or a suitable larger volume if the content of soluble solids is low, in a silica, porcelain or platinum dish and gently ignite the residue at a temperature not exceeding 500° C. Add 1 ml of concentrated hydrochloric acid and 10 ml of distilled water and evaporate again to dryness.

Dissolve the residue in the dish in distilled water and dilute to 100 ml. Place a 250-ml conical flask under the chromatographic tube, remove the stopper and allow 50 ml of the solution to pass through the column. When the water level has sunk nearly to the level of the bed, transfer the remainder of the solution to the tube. When this has nearly passed into the column, wash the bulb with two separate 50-ml portions of distilled water in a similar manner and stopper the bulb as described above.

Add 1 drop of each of indicator solutions A and B to the eluate in the flask and titrate with 0·02 N sodium hydroxide solution to a grey colour.

Calculate the total cationic content as calcium carbonate.

$$\text{1 ml of } 0·02 \ N \text{ NaOH} \equiv 1·0 \text{ mg of CaCO}_3.$$

PROCEDURE FOR DETERMINING ALKALI METALS—

Determine the content of the alkali metals either by flame photometry (see Appendix), or as follows.

Measure 250 ml of the sample into a small beaker. Raise the temperature to the boiling-point and add 1 ml of phenolphthalein indicator solution; then add small quantities of solid barium hydroxide until the colour change indicates a slight excess, care being taken to avoid violent boiling. Remove the precipitate by filtering through a Whatman No. 40 filter-paper, washing it twice, and collect the filtrate and washings in a 250-ml beaker. Add 1 ml of ammonium hydroxide and then ammonium carbonate solution in slight excess. Cover the beaker and boil the mixture. Filter off the precipitate, wash it with distilled water and collect the filtrate and washings in a weighed silica, platinum or porcelain dish. Evaporate the solution to dryness, make the residue slightly acid with sulphuric acid and evaporate again to dryness. Ignite the residue until no more fumes are evolved. The residue consists of alkali-metal sulphates. Cool and weigh the dish. Assuming that 1 mg of residue ≡ 0·7 mg of calcium carbonate, calculate the calcium carbonate equivalent to the alkali-metal sulphates.

CALCULATION OF TOTAL HARDNESS—

Deduct the value obtained for the alkali metals from that obtained for total cations and calculate the total hardness, in terms of calcium carbonate, as milligrams per litre of sample.

METHOD B

PRINCIPLE OF METHOD—

The method consists in determining the amount of standard mixed alkali required to precipitate the "non-alkaline" cations.

REAGENTS—

Hydrochloric acid, 0·1 N.

Hydrochloric acid, 0·5 N.

Mixed alkali solution, 0·5 N—Dissolve 14 g of anhydrous sodium carbonate in about 300 ml of distilled water; also dissolve 11 g of sodium hydroxide in about 300 ml of distilled water. Mix the two solutions and dilute to 1 litre. Determine the normality of the solution by titrating 25 ml with 0·5 N hydrochloric acid, using methyl orange indicator solution. Adjust the solution to 0·5 N if necessary.

Sodium hydroxide solution, 0·1 N.
Sodium hydroxide solution, 0·5 N.
Methyl orange indicator solution—A 0·04 per cent. aqueous solution.

PROCEDURE—

Measure a suitable volume (usually 100 to 250 ml) of the filtered effluent sample into a conical flask, add 0·2 ml (about 4 drops) of methyl orange indicator solution and neutralise with 0·1 N hydrochloric acid or 0·1 N sodium hydroxide solution, as appropriate.

Measure into a 100-ml porcelain basin exactly 10 ml of the mixed alkali solution. Add some of the neutralised sample, and evaporate the solution at a temperature just below the boiling-point, replacing the water lost by evaporation by more of the neutralised sample until all has been used. Wash the flask with distilled water and add the washings to the liquid in the basin; continue the evaporation until the volume of the liquid is reduced to about 25 ml.

Filter the solution and collect the filtrate in the original flask. Thoroughly wash the basin with three successive amounts, each of about 5 ml, of hot distilled water, added from a fine jet, and transfer the washings to the filter, allowing each portion to pass through the filter before adding the next. Wash the filter three times with a fine jet of hot distilled water, using about 5 ml each time, and again allow each washing to pass completely through the filter. Cool the filtrate and titrate it with 0·5 N hydrochloric acid. Express the total hardness (*a*), as milligrams per litre of sample.

$$\text{Total hardness} = \frac{(10 - \text{Volume of } 0\cdot5 \, N \text{ acid, ml}) \times 25 \times 1000}{\text{Volume of sample taken, ml}}.$$

CALCULATION OF TEMPORARY HARDNESS—

If the original sample is acid, there is no temporary hardness.
If the original sample is alkaline, calculate the alkalinity (*b*) from the formula—

$$\frac{\text{Volume of } 0\cdot1 \, N \text{ hydrochloric acid required, ml} \times 5 \times 1000}{\text{Volume of sample taken, ml}}.$$

If the total hardness (*a*) exceeds (*b*), the value for (*b*) is the temporary hardness.

If (*b*) exceeds (*a*), there is no permanent hardness and the temporary hardness is given by (*a*).

Calcium and Magnesium

PRINCIPLE OF METHOD—

The method consists in determining calcium separately, and the sum of the calcium and magnesium; magnesium is then calculated by difference. Lead, which would otherwise interfere, is removed as sulphate.

APPLICABILITY—

The method is generally applicable.

REAGENTS—

EDTA solution—Dissolve 3·72 g of crystalline disodium ethylenediamine-tetra-acetate dihydrate (EDTA) in distilled water and dilute to 1 litre.
Hydrochloric acid, sp.gr. 1·18.
Sodium hydroxide solution, 4 M—Dissolve 16 g of sodium hydroxide in 100 ml of distilled water.
Potassium cyanide solution, 10 per cent. *w/v*.
Ammonium hydroxide, dilute—A 10 per cent. aqueous solution of ammonium hydroxide, sp.gr. 0·880.
Buffer solution of pH 10·0—Dissolve 67·5 g of ammonium chloride in 570 ml of ammonium hydroxide, sp.gr. 0·880, and dilute to 950 ml. Dissolve 0·616 g of

magnesium sulphate, $MgSO_4.7H_2O$, and 0·93 g of disodium ethylenediaminetetra-acetate dihydrate in 50 ml of distilled water. Mix the two solutions.

The use of 2 ml of buffer solution in 100 ml of the effluent sample is equivalent to 5 mg per litre of magnesium in terms of calcium carbonate together with its equivalent of EDTA.

Sodium sulphate solution—A 10 per cent. w/v solution of the anhydrous salt.

Solochrome black WDFA indicator solution—Dissolve 0·5 g of Solochrome black WDFA (Eriochrome black T) and 4·5 g of hydroxylamine hydrochloride in 100 ml of 95 per cent. ethanol (or industrial methylated spirit). This solution does not deteriorate within 1 month if kept in the dark.

Murexide indicator—Mix thoroughly 0·20 g of murexide and 100 g of sodium chloride. The indicator is used in solid form.

Methyl orange indicator solution—A 0·04 per cent. w/v aqueous solution.

Bromophenol blue indicator solution—A 0·04 per cent. w/v solution in 95 per cent. ethanol (or industrial methylated spirit).

PROCEDURE FOR CALCIUM—

Evaporate 200 ml or a suitable quantity of the effluent sample in a silica, porcelain or platinum dish. Gently ignite the residue at a temperature not exceeding 500° C. Add 1 ml of concentrated hydrochloric acid and 10 ml of distilled water. Add 5 ml of sodium sulphate solution, boil gently for 10 minutes, cool and filter into a 100-ml calibrated flask. Wash the dish and filter-paper and dilute the filtrate to the mark. Measure 50 ml of the solution, neutralise with the sodium hydroxide solution, using methyl orange as indicator, and add 1 ml in excess; then add 5 ml of potassium cyanide solution. Transfer the liquid to a large white dish. Add approximately 0·2 g of murexide indicator, and titrate with EDTA solution until the colour becomes violet. The end-point is indicated when a further addition of 0·1 ml of EDTA solution produces no further colour change. Express the result as milligrams of calcium per litre of sample.

1 ml of EDTA solution ≡ 0·4 mg of calcium.

PROCEDURE FOR MAGNESIUM—

Transfer the remaining 50 ml of the solution to a white dish and neutralise to litmus paper with ammonium hydroxide. Add 5 ml of potassium cyanide solution, 2 ml of the buffer solution and 6 drops of the Solochrome black WDFA indicator solution. Titrate the solution with EDTA solution until the colour becomes blue.

Calculate the sum of the calcium and magnesium so obtained in terms of calcium. Deduct the calcium value obtained from the previous titration and calculate the difference as magnesium. Express the result as milligrams of magnesium per litre of sample.

Calcium × 0·6 = magnesium.

Non-volatile Matter Extractable by Light Petroleum

The commonly used terms "oil," "fat," "grease" and so on do not form a sufficiently precise basis on which to found a comprehensive method of analysis. No solvent is known that will selectively extract only fatty or hydrocarbon oils; the term "non-volatile matter extracted by light petroleum" is recommended, since this will normally include fatty and non-volatile hydrocarbon oils and greases, but the analyst must bear in mind that the extract may contain a variety of chemical substances that cannot properly be classified as either oil or grease.

Light petroleum is not a good solvent for bituminous substances, nor can it be used directly to determine volatile organic liquids such as petrol or benzene. If a determination of bituminous substances or of substances that are appreciably volatile at 100° C is required, special methods appropriate to the nature of the problem must be applied.

REAGENTS—

Magnesium sulphate solution—Dissolve 1 g of magnesium sulphate, $MgSO_4.7H_2O$, in 100 ml of distilled water.

Light petroleum, boiling range below 40° C.

Lime cream—Prepare a thin cream by mixing 2 g of calcium oxide with distilled water into a paste and dilute the suspension to 100 ml.

Hydrochloric acid, diluted $(1 + 3)$.

Sodium sulphate, anhydrous.

PROCEDURE—

Make a mark on the outside of the sample bottle at the level of the top of the contained liquid. If the sample includes a measurable layer of floating matter, carefully decant as much of it as possible into a 500-ml separating funnel (see Note 1) and return to the sampling bottle any water that separates. To the residue of the sample in the bottle add 5 ml of magnesium sulphate solution. Stir the liquid slowly in a rotary direction with a glass rod and cautiously add small volumes of lime cream (see Note 2), until flocculation occurs. Continue the stirring for about 2 minutes, then withdraw the glass rod, rinsing it with light petroleum, and collect the washings in the separating funnel containing the decanted liquid. Allow the precipitate in the sample bottle to settle. (This usually takes place fairly rapidly, but if a clear top layer does not begin to form within 5 minutes, see Note 2.) When the slurry has completely settled, siphon off the clear top layer to within about half an inch of the top of the precipitate. If any floating oil still remains in the top layer, leave this in the bottle. Dissolve the precipitate in diluted hydrochloric acid and pour the acid liquid into the separating funnel, taking care not to transfer any large adventitious solids (*e.g.*, twigs and leaves) that may be included with the sample. Wash the bottle with 50 ml of light petroleum and add this to the liquid in the funnel. Shake the funnel continuously but not vigorously for 1 minute. Allow the layers to separate, draw off the aqueous layer into a second separating funnel and extract it again with a further 50 ml of light petroleum. Withdraw and reject the aqueous layer and combine the two light-petroleum extracts in the first funnel. Draw off and reject any further water layer that may separate, add 2 g of powdered anhydrous sodium sulphate to the non-aqueous layer and shake at intervals over a period of about half an hour. Filter this layer through a 9-cm Whatman No. 30 filter-paper (see Note 3) into a previously weighed wide-necked flask having a capacity of 250 ml, covering the filter-paper with a clock-glass to reduce evaporation. Wash the paper with two successive 20-ml quantities of light petroleum, allowing the first washing to pass completely through the paper before adding the second. Distil off most of the light petroleum, finally evaporating the last traces in a current of warm air; then heat the flask on a boiling-water bath for exactly 10 minutes, dry the outside, cool and weigh. (If, after the solvent has evaporated, the residue contains visible water, add 2 ml of acetone, evaporate on a water bath, and repeat the addition and evaporation until all visible water has been removed.)

Determine the volume of the original sample in the bottle and express the amount of non-volatile matter extractable by light petroleum as milligrams per litre of sample.

NOTES—1. The taps of separating funnels should not be lubricated with matter that is soluble in light petroleum.

2. Some effluents do not readily flocculate with lime. For such effluents preliminary tests should be made with a fresh sample in order to find a suitable flocculating agent. The following are suggested—

Aluminium sulphate, 1 per cent. solution, with suitable adjustment of pH.
Ferric chloride, 1 per cent. solution, and ammonium hydroxide.
Zinc acetate, 10 per cent. solution, and potassium ferrocyanide, 5 per cent. solution.
Zinc acetate, 10 per cent. solution, and sodium carbonate, 5 per cent. solution.

3. This size of filter-paper is recommended, but it may be necessary to use a slightly larger paper if the light-petroleum extract contains much suspended matter.

Volatile Immiscible Liquids

PRINCIPLE OF METHOD—

This method[1] depends on the miscibility of volatile oils with acetone and their relative insolubility in water. The oils are removed from the sample in a current of air, adsorbed on activated carbon and then eluted with acetone. Dilution of the acetone solution with acid Teepol produces a turbidity varying in intensity with the amount of oil present: this turbidity is measured against standards.

RANGE—

For volatile oil contents of between 3 and 500 mg per litre of sample.

APPARATUS—

Absorption tube—A small cylindrical or thistle funnel with a stem about 18 to 20 cm long and 0·5 cm in diameter. The stem is fitted with a rubber stopper that will fit tightly into the upper end of a reflux condenser.

A 2-necked flask having a capacity of about 1·5 litres, fitted with a reflux condenser in one neck and with an air-delivery tube, reaching to the bottom of the flask, in the other.

Matched test-tubes (6 inch × ⅝ inch), graduated at 2 ml and 10 ml.

REAGENTS—

Acid Teepol solution—A solution containing 1 ml of sulphuric acid, sp.gr. 1·84, and 1 ml of Teepol per litre of distilled water. Cool to between 5° and 10° C before use.

*Activated carbon.**

Sodium hydroxide solution—A 10 per cent. w/v solution of the analytical-reagent grade in distilled water.

Acetone—Analytical-reagent grade.

PROCEDURE FOR DETERMINING VOLATILE OIL IN THE RANGE 3 TO 15 MG PER LITRE—

Weigh 0·2 g of activated carbon and pack it lightly between tight plugs of glass-wool in the narrow stem of the absorption tube. Arrange the flask and condenser for reflux distillation in a current of air and fit the absorption tube into the outlet end of the apparatus (Fig. 2).

Samples of effluent or river water in which oils are to be determined should be collected with precautions to ensure that they are representative and should be contained in wide-necked bottles of clear glass, holding approximately 1 litre. (See "Sampling."). Mark the level of the liquid on the outside of the bottle for subsequent determination of the volume, and pour all the sample into the distillation

* Obtainable from Messrs. Sutcliffe, Speakman & Co. Ltd., Leigh, Lancashire, quality No. 207, type B, B.S. mesh 20 to 40.

flask.   Rinse out the bottle with two 2·5-ml portions of acetone, taking care that the acetone dissolves any traces of oil left adhering to the inside of the sample bottle; pour the acetone into the distillation flask.   Add sodium hydroxide solution to raise the pH of the sample to approximately 10.   Connect the gas-delivery tube to the flask and pass a current of air through the sample at such a rate that the bubbles can just be counted; gently boil the liquid.   About 10 minutes after drops of acetone can no longer be observed forming in the condenser, discontinue heating the flask and remove the absorption tube containing the carbon.   Wash the carbon with acetone, added drop by drop, and collect the filtrate in one of the graduated test-tubes.   When exactly 2 ml of acetone have been collected, dilute the filtrate to the 10-ml mark with acid Teepol solution.

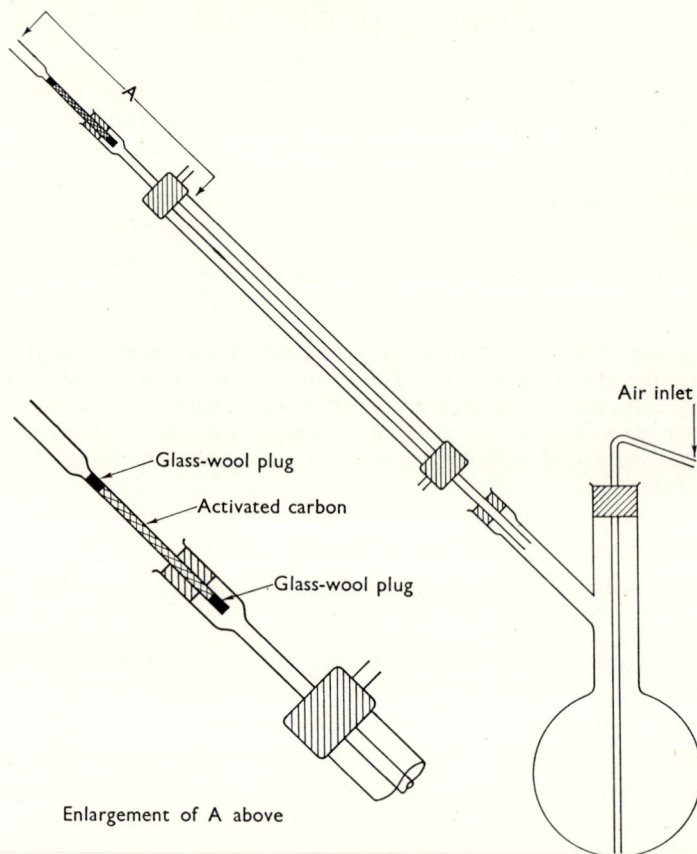

Air inlet

Glass-wool plug

Activated carbon

Glass-wool plug

Enlargement of A above

Fig. 2.   Adsorption apparatus

Preparation of standards—Prepare a solution containing 1·00 ml of petrol, sp.gr. 0·73 (or other volatile oil—see Note), dissolved in 100 ml of acetone.   From a microburette measure into a series of the graduated test-tubes 0·4, 0·8, 1·2, 1·6 and 2·0 ml of this solution and dilute to the 2-ml mark with acetone.   Finally dilute each of the standards to the 10-ml mark with acid Teepol solution and match the turbidity of sample visually against these standards.

Express the volatile oil content in terms of milligrams of petrol (or other reference oil) per litre of sample.

NOTE—Equal weights (or volumes) of different classes of commercial fuel oils do not give the same degrees of turbidity when subjected to the above procedure, but variations between different oils of roughly the same category, *e.g.*, kerosene and white spirit, or two different brands of petrol, are insignificant. For the most accurate work, therefore, it is necessary to prepare comparison standards with oil of the type that is present in the sample. The classes of oil likely to be present in effluents can usually be closely identified by their odour. An alternative procedure, if identification is impossible, is to refer the sample to some arbitrary standard, such as petrol or white spirit, on the same principle that "phenols" in water are usually referred to hydroxybenzene. This may lead to some sacrifice of accuracy, which, however, is not likely to be of practical importance.

PROCEDURE FOR DETERMINING OILS IN THE RANGE 12 TO 40 mg PER LITRE—

The apparatus and reagents are as described above, but 50-ml graduated cylinders should be used instead of test-tubes.

Pack 1 g of carbon into the stem of the small funnel and transfer the oil to the carbon by volatilising it in the manner already prescribed. At the end of this operation extract the oil from the carbon with successive 1-ml quantities of acetone, collecting the filtrate in a 50-ml graduated cylinder. When exactly 5 ml of filtrate have passed through the carbon, dilute the acetone to 50 ml with acid Teepol solution.

Preparation of standards—Prepare, as before, a 1 per cent. v/v solution of the reference oil in acetone. From a burette measure into a series of 50-ml graduated cylinders 1·0, 2·0, 3·0, 4·0 and 5·0 ml of this solution and dilute to the 5-ml mark with acetone. Finally dilute each of the standards to 50 ml with acid Teepol solution and match the sample against these standards, either instrumentally or visually.

PROCEDURE FOR DETERMINING QUANTITIES OF OILS IN EXCESS OF 40 mg PER LITRE—

If quantities of volatile oil in excess of 40 mg per litre are present, the final turbidity will be too dense to measure. This difficulty cannot be overcome by making the determination on only a portion of the sample, as it is impossible to distribute floating oil uniformly. The following method is suitable—

After all the volatile oil from a fresh sample has been absorbed on the carbon, as already described, extract the oil from the carbon with successive small volumes of acetone. Dilute the acetone solution to a measured volume and, on a suitable aliquot of this solution, determine the turbidity, using the standards as described for the range 12 to 40 mg per litre.

REFERENCE

1. Sherratt, J. G., *Analyst*, 1956, **81**, 518.

Oxygen Demand

Introduction

The ultimate purification of an effluent from organic matter must be by a process of oxidation. The assessment of the amount of oxygen necessary for this purpose has been the subject of much research over many years, but it is still true to say that no one single procedure has been devised that will give a satisfactory and complete determination of the requirements for all effluents and in all circumstances. Many methods or variations of these have been suggested during the past hundred years, but only three selected methods are recommended and described; two are essentially chemical in character and one is biochemical. Mention should also be made of the theoretical calculation of the total oxygen requirement of an effluent, which can be derived from a knowledge of the contents of the elements in it existing in oxidisable forms. This quantity has been termed the "Ultimate Oxygen Demand" (U.O.D.). When the main elements involved are carbon and nitrogen, the expression U.O.D. $= 2 \cdot 67C + 4 \cdot 57N$ has been suggested, where C is the organic carbon content and N is the sum of the ammoniacal and organic nitrogen contents. It must be pointed out, however, that other elements may also exert an oxygen demand, *e.g.*, hydrogen, sulphur and phosphorus. For strict accuracy these should also be taken into account and allowance should be made for the oxygen already present in organic combination.

The methods of assessment of the oxygen demand described are the determination of—

(a) oxygen absorbed from boiling acid potassium dichromate (dichromate value),
(b) oxygen absorbed from acid potassium permanganate (permanganate value), and
(c) Biochemical Oxygen Demand (B.O.D.).

Although these are dealt with in detail in the following sections, it is convenient to summarise here the main considerations with regard to their applicability and limitations.

DICHROMATE VALUE—

The use of potassium dichromate in boiling acid solution for determining the chemical oxygen demand of effluents was introduced by Adeney and Dawson[1] in 1926 and much subsequent research has been devoted to it. It is convenient to adopt the term "Dichromate Value"* as an abbreviated title for this test. As in the permanganate procedure, it must be stressed that the chemical oxygen demand as determined by the test represents the requirement for only part of the organic matter; the carbonaceous matter may not be completely oxidised and the organic nitrogen is generally unoxidised, the proportion depending on the structure of the organic compounds present. Chemical oxidation of this nature does not differentiate between the biochemically unstable and stable organic matter; therefore, chemical oxygen demand values are not strictly correlated with biochemical oxygen demand.

Nevertheless, the dichromate-value test, which is a new feature in British practice, is recommended as a standard method, since, for trade effluents, it has considerable advantages over the permanganate-value test, particularly in regard to reproducibility and to its applicability to a wide variety of samples.

* In the tenth edition of "Standard Methods for the Examination of Water, Sewage and Industrial Wastes,"[2] the result of the dichromate-value test is expressed as the "Chemical Oxygen Demand" of the sample.

PERMANGANATE VALUE—

The oxygen absorbed from acid potassium permanganate is the oldest of the tests now in use. It is convenient to adopt the term "Permanganate Value" as an abbbreviated title for this test. Its continued use in the British Isles is due to its simplicity, which enables it to be carried out by operators without a high degree of skill, and it also gives a result that is available on the same day. It was one of the earliest methods used to assess pollution and therefore provides a continuing basis for comparison with the results obtained in previous years. In most cases it is suitable for routine control in any particular works, and is one of the methods that may be used when a B.O.D. determination is inadmissible, for example, by reason of toxicity to seeding organisms of the materials under examination.

The scope of the test is limited; it is an empirical measure of chemically oxidisable matter, although, as a general rule, nitrogenous substances remain unoxidised. The result is only very broadly related to either the ultimate biochemical or chemical oxygen demands, the relationship varying with the chemical substances present in the sample.

In order to ensure that all the results obtained are comparable, it is imperative that the conditions specified shall be rigorously observed.

BIOCHEMICAL OXYGEN DEMAND—

The B.O.D. test was devised as the result of the researches made in this country under the auspices of the Royal Commission on Sewage Disposal. It is, in fact, a biological procedure that attempts to simulate the natural process of purification of organic matter by oxidation as it occurs in a river or stream, where the dissolved oxygen in the water supplies the oxygen used by the organic matter and is itself replaced in the water by the absorption of oxygen from the air at the air - water interface or surface. The duration of the test is 5 days and it must be stressed that in that time only a part of the total oxygen required for the complete oxidation of the organic matter will be used up. Moreover, during the 5 days, the carbonaceous matter will be preferentially oxidised, since the oxidation of the nitrogenous portion to nitrite or nitrate generally occurs at a later stage. Particularly for river and stream surveys and also for sewage-effluent assessment this is a most useful test, but with industrial wastes great caution must be observed, since the up-take of oxygen in the B.O.D. test is due to biological oxidation of organic matter, and the presence of any substance that depresses or inhibits biological activity interferes. Such substances include chlorine, chloramines, certain metallic compounds and organic substances that may be bactericidal when present in concentrations above a particular level.

After careful consideration the Joint Committee concluded that, in the interests of uniformity and for convenience of operation in the many laboratories that require to assess biochemical oxygen demand on both trade and sewage effluents, it was desirable that the method recommended should, so far as is possible, be identical in detail with that recommended by the Ministry of Housing and Local Government Committee for the Analysis of Sewage and Sewage Effluents. Permission was therefore obtained from H.M. Stationery Office to reproduce this method, although it has, of course, been necessary to make certain deletions and additions to the text in order to cover the special problems associated with trade effluents. The Joint Committee, therefore, put forward the revised text that appears in a following section—the deletions and additions to the Ministry method being duly indicated (see footnote, p. 27). These remarks also apply to the section on "Dissolved Oxygen," which is a necessary preliminary to the B.O.D. determination.

TABLE IIA

EFFECT OF INHIBITORY SUBSTANCES ON THE DETERMINATION OF THE B.O.D. OF SEWAGE BY THE DILUTION METHOD

Interfering substance or ion	Concentration in B.O.D. bottle,* mg per litre	Effect on B.O.D. of sewage		Reference
		Reduction, %	Qualitative effect	
Sodium arsenate (as Na_3AsO_4) ..	up to 100	—	Little effect	3
Chloramine {	0·005	9†		4
	0·005	4‡		4
Tervalent chromium (as Cr) {	1	10		5
	4	67		6
Sexavalent chromium (as Cr)	0·1	—	Inhibited nitrification	7
	0·3	—	Had little effect on carbonaceous oxidation	7
	0·45	8†		4
	0·45	10‡		4
	0·9	20		7
	1·0	10		5
	4·0	70		6
Cobalt chloride (as Co)	0·9	5		3
Copper (as Cu) {	0·01	5		7
	0·05	20	Inhibited nitrification	7
	0·1	8†		4
	0·1	7‡		4
	0·4	42		3
Cyanide (as CN) {	0·1	5		8
	0·3	5		9
	0·8	22		3
	1·0	40		8
	2·0	38		3
	25	100		9
Lead (as Pb) {	0·2	6†		4
	0·2	5‡		4
Mercuric chloride (as $HgCl_2$)	0·025	20		5
	0·5	35†		4
	0·5	37‡		4
	1·0	90		3
	2·0	100		5
Sea water ..	—	—	Rate of biochemical oxidation of sewage appeared to be greatest at a salinity of 8·5 g per 1000 g (= about 25 per cent. of sea water), but in one experiment the rate was greatest at a salinity of 22·7 g per 1000 g	10
	—	—	5-day B.O.D. of polluted estuary water was usually greatest at a salinity of about 20 g per 1000 g, but with some samples was greatest at a salinity of below 5 g per 1000 g	11

* In the manometric method (see Table IIB) the sample is usually undiluted, but in the dilution method the sample may be diluted 50 to 100 times with synthetic dilution water.

† Reduction in B.O.D. of a solution containing 300 mg of glucose per litre, synthetic dilution water being used.

‡ Reduction in B.O.D. of a solution containing 300 mg of glutamic acid per litre, synthetic dilution water being used.

In addition, the following points merit special attention—

(a) The question of "seeding" is of great importance in a B.O.D. method for trade effluents, but it presents considerable difficulties; appropriate paragraphs on this subject are included in the text (see pp. 38 and 39).

(b) It has already been mentioned that substances that depress or inhibit biological action interfere with the B.O.D. test. A list of inorganic substances that have been reported to interfere in this way in the B.O.D. test for sewage is given in Tables IA and IB. Some organic compounds may be inhibitory and others may not respond to the test because their molecular structure renders them resistant to biological attack. Lists of organic compounds, including most of the active agents of synthetic detergents,[12,13,14,15] whose behaviour in the dilution and manometric B.O.D. tests has been examined, are to be found in the technical literature.[16,17,18,19,20,21]

TABLE IIB

EFFECT OF INHIBITORY SUBSTANCES ON THE DETERMINATION OF THE
B.O.D. OF SEWAGE BY THE MANOMETRIC METHOD

Interfering substance or ion	Concentration in undiluted sewage, mg per litre	Effect on amount of oxygen taken up by sewage in 5 days		Reference
		Reduction, %	Qualitative effect	
Cadmium (as Cd) ..	5	16		22
Cobalt (as Co) ..	5	24	Caused initial retardation	22
Copper (as Cu) ..	1	22		22
Tervalent chromium (as Cr) {	up to 20	—	Little effect	6
	25	14		22
Sexavalent chromium (as Cr) {	up to 20	—	Little effect	6
	10	3		22
	25	10		22
Ferric chloride (as FeCl₃)	5*	13†		23
Nickel (as Ni) ..	5	24	Caused an initial lag of 1 day	22
Zinc (as Zn) ..	5	12		22

* Plus sodium bicarbonate to adjust the pH to 7·8.
† In 6 days.

(c) In addition to the standard dilution method, manometric methods for determining B.O.D. are discussed in general terms (see p. 42). Such methods are especially useful for trade effluents.

(d) Consideration was given to oxygen absorption, which, although measured in the 5-day B.O.D. test, may not be biological in character but rather a direct chemical oxidation, e.g., that of fine metallic particles or readily oxidisable inorganic compounds. If it is desired to differentiate between the true biological and chemical oxidation, this may be done by using chloroform as an inhibitor of biological action, and carrying out duplicate determinations with and without the addition of chloroform.

(e) Compounds that interfere with the determination of dissolved oxygen by the Winkler method also interfere with the B.O.D. test; these include oxidising and reducing compounds, which either liberate iodine from potassium iodide or reduce liberated iodine, and some other compounds that have been reported to cause interference, as follows—

Chromate—This liberates iodine from potassium iodide. Since the oxygen consumed in the B.O.D. test is a difference figure, Placak, Ruchhoft and Snapp[7] consider that this should not introduce an error, particularly when the concentration of chromate is low.

C

Gas liquor—Abbott and Fearn[24] state that the dissolved oxygen in dilutions of sewage plus gas liquor cannot be determined by the Rideal - Stewart modification (see p. 31); the azide method could be used instead.

Miscellaneous substances—Heukelekian[3] states that the following substances, at the concentrations stated, interfere seriously with the unmodified Winkler method (see p. 28)—

Substance	Concentration, mg per litre
Gasoline	1000 (slightly at 100)
Phenol	50 (slightly at 10)
Sodium arsenite	8
Potassium dichromate	100
Potassium chromate	10
Strychnine	100

Interference by sodium arsenite can be overcome by using the Rideal - Stewart modification.

Sulphur dioxide and sulphites—Tyler and Gunter[25] state that sulphur dioxide and sulphites interfere in the unmodified Winkler determination, and that the hypochlorite modification does not overcome the interference.

Dichromate Value

(Oxygen absorbed from boiling acid potassium dichromate solution)

Potassium dichromate in acid solution was first used by Adeney and Dawson[1] to determine the chemical oxygen demand of polluted waters. The method has since been studied and improved by Abbott,[26] Ingols and Murray,[27] Moore, Kroner and Ruchhoft[28] and by others[29,30,31,32,33] and, since the introduction of the use of silver sulphate,[32] the results obtained have been found to be very close to the theoretical value for a large number of organic compounds. This finding was in marked contrast to those obtained by the traditional method in which potassium permanganate is used.

The relevant Panel of the Joint Committee therefore considered the two methods in detail. Some comparative tests were carried out during this investigation and the details and results are reported in a paper by Cameron and Moore.[34]

The dichromate-value test has other advantages besides yielding results that are often close to the theoretical value. One of these advantages is that a considerably shorter time is required to carry out a test—2 hours at the most—than is required for determining the permanganate value. Again, because the test is carried out at the boiling-point, errors caused by temperature differences do not arise and there is no need for a thermostatically controlled bath. The apparatus used is slightly more complicated than that necessary for the permanganate-value test, but it is still of a type that is readily available in every laboratory.

Finally, it should be noted that the inclusion in a collection of recommended methods of a procedure for determining the dichromate value is an entirely new feature in British practice. This is done in the belief, supported by the experimental work carried out, that the test is worthy of greater notice than it has hitherto received.

DEFINITION—

The dichromate value is expressed as the number of milligrams of oxygen absorbed from standard dichromate per litre of sample.

RANGE—

(*a*) In the *absence* of chloride, for dichromate values down to 50 mg per litre.

(*b*) In the *presence* of chloride, the method is applicable when the number of milligrams of oxygen absorbed per litre (*i.e.*, dichromate value) is greater than one-quarter of the number of milligrams of chloride present per litre. (See Note 1.)

APPLICABILITY—

The method is generally applicable. However, chloride ion (if present in amounts greater than four times the dichromate value) and certain nitrogenous organic substances (*e.g.*, urea) interfere. Details are given at the end of the "Procedure" for determining the correction to be applied for the amount of nitrogen oxidised, and this should be determined each time when accurate results are required. However, for routine analyses of an effluent, a preliminary check need only be made to ascertain whether, and to what extent, the nitrogen has been oxidised: if the result is negative, then the method is applicable without modification.

REAGENTS—

Silver sulphate solution—A 1·25 per cent. solution in 50 per cent. v/v sulphuric acid.
Sulphuric acid, sp.gr. 1·84.
Potassium dichromate solution, 0·1 N.
Ferrous sulphate solution, 0·1 N—Dissolve 27·8 g of the pure salt, $FeSO_4.7H_2O$, in a mixture of 25 ml of sulphuric acid and 75 ml of distilled water, and dilute with distilled water to 1 litre. This solution must be standardised at frequent intervals against the potassium dichromate solution, and its factor determined.
Ferrous - 1 : 10-phenanthroline indicator solution—Dissolve 0·695 g of ferrous sulphate, $FeSO_4.7H_2O$, in 100 ml of distilled water, add 1·485 g of 1 : 10-phenanthroline monohydrate and shake until dissolved.

PROCEDURE—

First determine the chloride content of the effluent sample in terms of 0·1 N silver nitrate (see "Determination of Chloride (Chlorion)").

Transfer a suitable volume of the effluent sample (25 or 50 ml) to a 500-ml round-bottomed flask having a standard B24 ground neck, and add to it the volume of 0·1 N potassium dichromate solution equal to the volume of 0·1 N silver nitrate required to combine with the chloride in the same volume of sample; then add a further 25 ml of potassium dichromate solution. Add an amount of sulphuric acid equal to the total (aqueous) volume multiplied by 1·2. Fit a suitable reflux condenser to the flask. Mix the solution well and boil it under reflux for at least $\frac{1}{2}$ hour. At the end of this period, add 10 ml of silver sulphate solution and allow the heating under reflux to continue for a further $1\frac{1}{2}$ hours. (See Note 2.)

Dilute the solution with a volume of distilled water equal to the original (total) aqueous volume multiplied by 4·5. Titrate with the ferrous sulphate solution, using a ferrous - 1 : 10-phenanthroline indicator solution; let this titre be T_1.

Treat in the same manner a volume of distilled water equal to the volume of sample taken, but omitting that volume of potassium dichromate solution added to deal with chloride; let this titre be T_2.

From the titration difference $(T_1 - T_2)$, calculate the net volume of dichromate used by the oxidation and then calculate the dichromate value in terms of milligrams of oxygen absorbed per litre of sample.

1 ml of 0·1 N potassium dichromate solution ≡ 0·8 mg of oxygen.

MODIFICATION FOR INTERFERENCE BY NITROGENOUS ORGANIC SUBSTANCES—

A determination of the total unoxidised nitrogen is carried out on (*a*) the final solution obtained above after titration, (*b*) a fresh portion of the sample equal in volume to that originally taken and (*c*) the titrated blank. The difference between (*a*) and (*b*), after correction for the blank, gives the loss of nitrogen incurred during the dichromate-value test.

The loss of nitrogen may take place through more than one chemical route, but it appears that tervalent nitrogen is involved. Therefore—

1 ml of $0 \cdot 1$ N potassium dichromate solution $\equiv 0 \cdot 467$ mg of nitrogen.

Procedure—Evaporate to white fumes of sulphuric acid the test and blank solutions obtained after titration, and continue heating until the solutions are clear green in colour.

Proceed to determine the total unoxidised nitrogen in both solutions, as described under "Determination of Total Unoxidised Nitrogen."

In addition, determine directly the total unoxidised nitrogen in a fresh portion of the effluent sample equal in volume to that originally taken.

Correction to be applied—For each $0 \cdot 467$ mg of nitrogen lost, deduct $0 \cdot 8$ mg of oxygen from the total amount of absorbed oxygen determined as above.

NOTES—1. Chloride, which is present in most trade effluents, introduces two sources of error.

In the first place, dichromate oxidises chloride to free chlorine and it is shown[34] that this oxidation is neither complete nor consistent, although always of a high degree. A consistent correction cannot, therefore, be applied. It should be appreciated that an assumption of 100 per cent. oxidation of chloride transfers an error to the concurrent oxidations and the magnitude of this transferred error depends on the relationship of chloride content to that of other oxidisable matter.

In the second place, the chlorine developed in the foregoing oxidation oxidises nitrogenous matter to elementary nitrogen. Hence, nitrogenous matter may be simultaneously oxidised directly by dichromate and indirectly by the chlorine developed, the latter oxidation being the greater. There is some evidence that tervalent nitrogen is involved and the nitrogen correction is based on this assumption: nevertheless, because of the simultaneous reactions taking place, the correction is not precise.

This indirect oxidation, although depending on the presence of chloride, is independent of the chloride concentration; the chlorine is reduced to chloride in performing the oxidation, thereby generating a cyclic reaction so long as nitrogenous matter responsive to this oxidation remains.

2. Experience may show that for some effluents the second reflux time may be reduced to 30 minutes.

Permanganate Value

(*Oxygen absorbed from acid potassium permanganate solution*)

The concentration of the permanganate solution used is usually $N/80$, but for trade wastes a concentration of $N/8$ is sometimes used (see Note, p. 26). The standard time for the test is 4 hours, but for some purposes a supplementary 3-minute test is made, and the relation between the 4-hour and the 3-minute tests may be a useful guide to the type of waste being examined.

It is desirable to use the same amounts of permanganate and of acid in all tests, the volume of sample being adjusted according to its estimated strength; also to make up the total volume used in any test to a fixed volume with water, and to adjust the volume of the sample so as to leave about one-half the permanganate unused. In practice, reductions between 30 and 70 per cent. are admissible.[35] The volume recommended is 50 ml of $N/80$ potassium permanganate, and the following figures show the volumes of sample usually necessary for a range of estimated permanganate values—

Permanganate value, mg per litre	25	50	100	125	250	500
Volume of sample, ml	100	50	25	20	10	5

When a small volume of sample is indicated, it is advisable to add it as a larger volume of a suitable dilution in order to ensure a representative distribution of suspended solids.

REAGENTS—

Potassium permanganate solution, approximately N/80—Dissolve 4·0 g of potassium permanganate in 1 litre of distilled water in a covered beaker and heat the solution to 90° to 95° C for 2 to 3 hours. Dilute to 10 litres with distilled water and store in the dark for some days to oxidise organic matter and to allow precipitated manganese dioxide to settle. Siphon or decant the supernatant liquid without disturbing the sediment, or filter through glass-wool or acid-digested and washed asbestos, or through a sintered-glass filter; the use of filter-paper is inadmissible. This solution must be stored in the dark, or in dark-glass bottles, and away from the risk of airborne dust or organic contamination.

Potassium permanganate solution, approximately N/8—Dissolve 4·0 g of potassium permanganate in 750 ml of hot water and heat to 90° to 95° C for 2 to 3 hours. Cool and dilute to 1 litre, and store in the dark for some days. Decant the supernatant liquid without disturbing the sediment or filter through glass-wool, acid-digested and washed asbestos, or through a sintered-glass filter. Store in the dark or in dark-glass bottles.

Potassium iodide solution, 10 per cent. w/v—Dissolve 10 g of potassium iodide in 100 ml of distilled water and store in a dark bottle. It is important that this solution shall remain colourless during the whole period that it is in use.

Potassium iodate solution, N/40—Dry analytical-reagent grade potassium iodate at 120° C, dissolve 0·892 g in distilled water and dilute to exactly 1 litre. This solution is stable for long periods if stored in a glass-stoppered bottle.

Sodium thiosulphate solution, approximately N/4—Dissolve 63 g of sodium thiosulphate, $Na_2S_2O_3.5H_2O$, in 1 litre of copper-free freshly boiled and cooled distilled water. Stabilise the solution by the addition of 1 ml of chloroform or 10 mg of mercuric iodide and allow to stand for several days before use.

Sodium thiosulphate solution, approximately N/80—Dilute 50 ml of *N*/4 sodium thiosulphate solution to 1 litre with copper-free freshly boiled and cooled distilled water, adding 1 ml of chloroform or 10 mg of mercuric iodide. Although reasonably stable if kept in a dark-glass bottle, it requires frequent standardisation against potassium iodate as follows—

Mix 5 ml of potassium iodide solution and 10 ml of dilute sulphuric acid and add 20 ml of *N*/40 potassium iodate solution, in that order, in a glass-stoppered flask. Add about 100 ml of distilled water. Titrate immediately with approximately *N*/80 sodium thiosulphate solution until the colour is pale yellow; add 2 or 3 drops of starch indicator solution and continue the titration until the blue colour just disappears.

1 ml of *N*/80 sodium thiosulphate solution ≡ 0·1 mg of oxygen.

Sulphuric acid, diluted (1 + 3)—Add gradually and cautiously 1 volume of sulphuric acid, sp.gr. 1·84, to three volumes of distilled water, mix and cool. Add *N*/80 potassium permanganate solution until a permanent faint pink colour is observed.

Starch indicator solution—Grind 1 g of soluble starch into a smooth paste with a little cold distilled water, and pour it into 1 litre of boiling distilled water with constant stirring. Boil for 1 minute, and allow to cool before use. This solution should be freshly prepared.

Stabilised starch indicator solution can be made by grinding 10 mg of mercuric iodide with the starch before adding the cold water, and then proceeding as described above: this solution can be used for some time after it is prepared. Alternatively,

0·1 g of thymol may be added to the boiling water used for making the solution.

> NOTE—As an alternative to starch solution, sodium starch glycollate solution, which is stable for many months, may be used. Between 1 and 2 ml of a 0·5 per cent. solution in cold distilled water may be added at the start of the titration, the approach to the end-point being shown by change from green to intense blue. At the end-point, which is sharp, the solution becomes colourless.

PROCEDURE FOR PERMANGANATE VALUE, BY 4-HOUR TEST—

Measure into a 12-oz glass-stoppered bottle 10 ml of diluted sulphuric acid and 50 ml of $N/80$ potassium permanganate solution. Select the volume of effluent sample to be used, and subtract it from 100 ml; add this final volume of distilled water to the acidified permanganate, raise the temperature of the solution to 27° C and add the volume of sample chosen, also at 27° C, and mix by gentle rotation of the bottle. Maintain the mixture at 27° C in a water bath or, after first raising the temperature to 27° C, in an incubator for 4 hours, re-mixing after 1 hour if much suspended matter is present.

After exactly 4 hours, add 5 ml of potassium iodide solution or approximately 0·5 g of potassium iodide, mix, and titrate with N/80 sodium thiosulphate, adding a few drops of starch indicator solution near the end-point. Continue the titration until the blue colour disappears, and ignore any blue colour that may return.

Carry out a blank determination, using distilled water instead of the sample.

Calculation—

Permanganate value (4-hour), mg per litre =

$$\frac{(\text{Vol. of } N/80 \text{ Na}_2\text{S}_2\text{O}_3 \text{ for blank, ml} - \text{vol. of } N/80 \text{ Na}_2\text{S}_2\text{O}_3 \text{ for test, ml}) \times 100}{\text{Vol. of sample taken, ml}}.$$

PROCEDURE FOR PERMANGANATE VALUE BY 3-MINUTE TEST—

Follow the same procedure as for the 4-hour test; it is essential to warm the effluent sample, the reagents and the distilled water to 27° C before mixing. Measure the permanganate and the acid into the bottle to be used for the test, and measure the requisite volumes of sample and distilled water into a separate container. Add the sample and the distilled water to the reagents, and mix by rotation. Maintain at 27° C for exactly 3 minutes, add the potassium iodide as in the 4-hour test, titrate, and calculate the permanganate value (3-minute) in the same manner.

INTERFERENCES—

Presence of nitrite—The test is affected by nitrite. A correction may be made by estimating the nitrite present and subtracting from the permanganate value a figure equivalent to the nitrite nitrogen $\times$ 1·14. If the amount of nitrite present is significant, the result should be returned as "permanganate value corrected for nitrite." It is, however, preferable to destroy the nitrite by the following procedure—

> Acidify the sample and the blank; add 1 g of urea to each and allow the solutions to stand for 5 minutes. Then add the appropriate volume of potassium permanganate solution and continue as in the "Procedure."

Presence of chromate—In the presence of acid and potassium iodide, chromates are reduced and decrease the permanganate value. A preliminary titration may be made with $N/80$ sodium thiosulphate after acid and potassium iodide solution have been added to a known volume of the sample, and the equivalent oxygen-absorption value added to the ascertained permanganate value.[36]

Presence of chloride—The use of phosphoric acid instead of sulphuric acid has been recommended in the presence of high concentrations of chloride.[37]

> NOTE: DETERMINATION OF THE PERMANGANATE VALUE BY USING $N/8$ POTASSIUM PERMANGANATE SOLUTION AT 27° C—
>
> When determining the permanganate value of trade wastes for calculation of the McGowan strength,[38] it is necessary to use $N/8$ potassium permanganate solution. There

has, in the past, been some latitude in procedure, but the method in general has been in line with the recommendations of the Royal Commission on Sewage Disposal,[38] *i.e.*, 10 ml of $N/8$ potassium permanganate, 10 ml of 10 per cent. sulphuric acid and a volume of the sample that leaves about one-half of the permanganate unabsorbed. The volume of sample generally used is 25 ml, or a smaller volume of sample made up to 25 ml; it is not customary to dilute to 100 ml, as in the 4-hour test. The volumes used in this test should be precisely stated.

After tests for permanganate value have been carried out, all bottles should immediately afterwards be washed with chromic acid, then with tap water and finally with distilled water.

Dissolved Oxygen*

PRINCIPLE OF METHOD—

The methods to be described for the determination of dissolved oxygen in water **or trade effluents** are based on the procedure originally devised by Winkler.[39] In this method the precipitation of manganous hydroxide is brought about in a glass-stoppered bottle completely filled with the sample under test. Any oxygen present in solution then quickly combines with the manganous hydroxide to form higher hydroxides, which, on subsequent acidification in the presence of iodide, liberate iodine in an amount chemically equivalent to the original dissolved-oxygen content of the sample. The iodine is then determined by titration with a standard solution of sodium thiosulphate.

The observance of adequate precautions when taking samples . . . . . is particularly important when they are required for dissolved-oxygen determinations.

SAMPLING AND APPARATUS—

Bottles—The bottle used should be of good quality, with a narrow neck and a well fitting ground-glass stopper, and should be of about 250 ml capacity. It is a great convenience if each bottle and its stopper is etched with a distinguishing number. The base of the stopper should be of such a shape that when the bottle is completely filled with water the stopper can be firmly inserted without trapping air bubbles. The bottles should be cleansed with chromic acid mixture (not soap or synthetic-detergent solutions) and then washed out several times with clean water.

Sampling—The method of collecting the sample should involve the least possible disturbance of the liquid. This is best accomplished with the aid of a special sampling arrangement (**see** "Sampling"), which ensures a several-fold displacement of the liquid in the sampling bottles without agitation with air bubbles.

If the percentage saturation of the sample with oxygen is to be determined, the temperature of the liquid at the moment of sampling and, if necessary, the barometric pressure should be noted.

Sampling apparatus—The sample must be collected without causing any change in the concentration of dissolved oxygen. Sometimes the liquid can be siphoned through a glass or rubber tube into the sample bottle; the tube should deliver to the bottom of the bottle and the liquid should be allowed to flow until the contents of the bottle have been changed several times.

* The methods described here for the Determination of Dissolved Oxygen and of Biochemical Oxygen Demand up to (but excluding) "Manometric Methods" (p. 42), but including "General Observations" (on p. 44), have been taken by permission of the Controller, H.M. Stationery Office, from "Chemical Analysis as Applied to Sewage and Sewage Effluents," Second Edition (1956), published by H.M.S.O. for the Ministry of Housing and Local Government. Departures from the text of the Ministry's methods (other than changes of a purely editorial nature made to ensure consistency with other methods in this series) are indicated by the use of **sans-serif type for reworded and new material,** and by groups of five dots (. . . . .) for omission.

The type of sampler . . . . . in common use . . . . . **is** the displacement sampler, consisting of a cylindrical container with a lead ring at the bottom, inside which the sample bottle is placed. The lid carries two tubes, one at the centre through which the water enters the bottle and another through which the displaced air leaves the container. These tubes are closed by small bungs attached to cords made fast to a line. While the sampler is being lowered to the desired depth, its weight is taken by a spring, also attached to the line. When the desired depth is reached, the line is jerked, thereby removing the bungs. Water then flows through the bottle until the container is full and the bottle is therefore washed out several times before the sample is taken. . . . .

When this displacement sampler is to be used at only a shallow depth, it is unnecessary to close the inlet and outlet tubes with bungs.

. . . . .

The temperature of the water should always be recorded immediately the sample is brought to the surface.

It is important to fix the dissolved oxygen in a sample immediately it is taken, as changes in the concentration of dissolved oxygen may occur rapidly both when the sample is sub-saturated and when it is super-saturated.

In the manipulations to be described in the ensuing sections, it is *extremely unwise* to suck the required amounts of reagents into pipettes, especially the alkaline iodide and sulphuric acid reagents. Dipping pipettes or pipettes fitted with rubber balls or teats should be used, and these will be found of very great convenience for field work. . . . .

DIRECT DETERMINATION AND MODIFICATIONS—

The Winkler method of determining dissolved oxygen is applicable only to relatively pure water. Many substances can interfere with the determination, and suitable modifications must be adopted to attain a reasonably accurate result. The commonest interfering substances are nitrites, ferrous salts, organic matter, sulphites, residual chlorine and suspended solids, and very considerable errors can be introduced in the determination if special precautions are not taken.

The two principal modifications of the original Winkler method are—

(a) The Alsterberg[40] or sodium azide procedure; this prevents interference by nitrite, but not by easily oxidised organic substances or inorganic substances (*e.g.*, ferrous iron, **if more than 1 mg per litre is present**).

(b) The Rideal - Stewart[41] or permanganate modification; this prevents interference by nitrite, by ferrous iron and by easily oxidised organic matter.

THE WINKLER METHOD

REAGENTS—

Manganous sulphate solution—Dissolve 500 g of manganous sulphate, $MnSO_4.4H_2O$, in distilled water, filter if necessary and dilute to 1 litre. . . . . The salt used should be free from ferric and manganic salts, *i.e.*, no iodine should be liberated when a portion of the salt is added to acidified potassium iodide solution.

Alkaline iodide solution—Prepare a solution containing 500 g of sodium hydroxide (or 700 g of potassium hydroxide) and 150 g of potassium iodide (or 140 g of sodium iodide) per litre. The alkali solution should be virtually free from carbonate, and the following method of preparation may be used. Dissolve the required weight of pure sodium hydroxide in its own weight of distilled water. When cool, transfer the solution to a bottle **preferably** coated internally with paraffin wax, close with a rubber stopper, and allow to stand quiescent for some days, during which any carbonate present sinks to the bottom. **Decant** the clear supernatant liquid. Now add the required quantity of potassium iodide dissolved in a small quantity of cold freshly boiled distilled water; dilute the mixture to the desired concentration with cold freshly boiled distilled water and mix.

Sulphuric acid, sp.gr. 1·84.

Potassium iodate solution, N/40—See p. 25.

Sodium thiosulphate solution, approximately N/4—Stock solution, see p. 25.

Sodium thiosulphate solution, approximately N/80—Working solution, see p. 25.

Starch indicator solution—See p. 25.

Procedure—

The following procedures apply to sample bottles of nominal capacity 250 ml. If a different size is used, the amounts of reagents must be adjusted accordingly.

To the sample of liquid taken as previously described, add 1 ml of manganous sulphate . . . . . solution, followed by 1 ml of alkaline iodide solution, the tips of the pipettes in each case being inserted well below the surface of the liquid. (The fine points of pipettes may be cut off so that they empty reasonably quickly.) Replace the stopper carefully so as to avoid inclusion of air bubbles, and thoroughly mix the contents by inverting and rotating the bottle several times.

The precipitate flocculates and settles fairly rapidly, but after the first mixing it will rarely be found that the top liquid is clear. A second period of inverting and rotating is necessary, both to clarify the liquid and to ensure that all the dissolved oxygen in the upper part of the bottle is absorbed. With **saline liquids**, a prolonged period of mixing may be necessary.

The precipitate is white if the sample was devoid of oxygen at the time of sampling, but becomes increasingly brown with rising oxygen content of the sample.

In the absence of organic matter the determination of the dissolved oxygen by acidification and titration may be postponed at this stage, provided that the bottles are kept in the dark. This is particularly convenient when the sampling for dissolved oxygen forms part of a survey in the field: the labelled bottles can be stored until the return to the laboratory. It is, of course, vital that air be excluded from the bottle during the period between precipitation and acidification; this should be assured if bottles with well fitting stoppers are used, but even then the period should not exceed a few hours.

Now add by pipette 1·5 ml of sulphuric acid, sp.gr. 1·84, re-stopper and well mix the contents by rotation. Some analysts prefer to acidify with 3 ml of 50 per cent. sulphuric acid, in order to avoid manipulations with the concentrated acid. Since solution of the precipitate is not rapid, allow sufficient time for this to take place. If necessary, continue to agitate by rotation until the precipitate dissolves before opening the bottle.

Transfer by pipette into a conical flask a suitable volume (say 100 ml from a 250-ml bottle) of the solution and immediately titrate the iodine with $N/80$ sodium thiosulphate solution, using as indicator 2 ml of starch indicator solution, which should be added towards the end of the titration. For very precise work an amperometric method may be used to detect the end-point in the titration of iodine with thiosulphate. Whichever method is used, however, it must be remembered that iodine is volatile and therefore the titration of its solution must be carried out as expeditiously as possible and with the minimum of exposure to the air.

. . . . .

Calculation—

$$\text{Dissolved oxygen, mg per litre} = \frac{\text{Volume of } N/80 \text{ sodium thiosulphate, ml} \times 100}{\text{Volume of sample titrated, ml}}.$$

There are two slight sources of error in this simplified calculation. One is due to the volume of sample displaced from the bottle by the reagents added, usually 3·5 ml for the 250-ml bottle. If great accuracy is required, the volume of the added reagents can be deducted from the volume of the bottle in making the calculation. The other source of error is that due to the presence of dissolved oxygen in the added reagents. This, however, has been determined[42,43] and is so small that it is negligible in the examination of trade effluents, although it may have to be taken into account in, for example, the examination of boiler-feed water.[44]

PRESENCE OF CERTAIN TYPES OF ORGANIC MATTER—

If the sample contains organic matter that is capable of direct oxidation by dissolved oxygen at pH values of about 12, corresponding to the degree of alkalinity produced when the alkaline iodide solution is added to a sample, then the sample should be acidified immediately the manganese hydroxide precipitate has settled sufficiently to give a layer of clear liquid near the top of the bottle. This procedure will give reliable results in the presence of organic matter corresponding to 1000 mg of dextrose or peptone per litre. If, say, about 5000 mg of such organic materials are present per litre, the samples should be acidified immediately after agitation, without waiting for the precipitate to settle.[45] As a guide to the time required for agitation, it may be mentioned that with 1 ml of manganous sulphate solution the time required for complete fixation of oxygen is 40 to 50 seconds; with double the quantity the time is halved.

THE ALSTERBERG OR SODIUM AZIDE MODIFICATION

When more than a trace of nitrite is present in a sample of liquid, it is not possible to obtain a satisfactory end-point to the iodine - thiosulphate titration, since nitrite in acid solution catalyses the liberation of iodine from iodide by dissolved oxygen. Hence the Winkler method is not directly applicable to waters containing nitrite. When nitrite, or ferrous iron at a concentration of less than 1 mg per litre, are the only interfering substances present, the Alsterberg modification is recommended for the determination of dissolved oxygen. In biochemical oxygen demand work, nitrites, even if absent at the start, may be formed during the incubation period. They may generally be expected in the effluents from biological oxidation processes.

Since nitrite is probably the most frequently encountered interfering substance, it is of great convenience for routine work if the reagent to eliminate it—sodium azide—is added in combination with the alkaline iodide solution. If nitrite is absent, the addition of azide is no disadvantage.

If the sample contains ferric salts, these may cause an error by interaction with the iodide. This can be avoided by carrying out the final acidification with 4 ml of 85 per cent. phosphoric acid.

The actual removal of nitrite takes place only after the acidification stage, i.e., the reaction is between nitrous acid and hydrazoic acid—

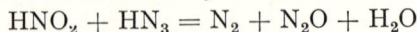

$$HNO_2 + HN_3 = N_2 + N_2O + H_2O$$

The azide and its decomposition products are indifferent to mild oxidising agents. It is essential that mineral acid be present, for in neutral or acetic acid solution the following reaction occurs—

$$2NaN_3 + I_2 = 2NaI + 3N_2$$

PROCEDURE—

Carry out the determination in exactly the same way as described for the Winkler method, but replace the alkaline iodide reagent by a solution containing 500 g of sodium hydroxide, 150 g of potassium iodide and 10 g of sodium azide per litre. Prepare the sodium hydroxide as previously described. Dissolve the potassium iodide and sodium azide separately in small amounts of distilled water. Add the iodide solution to the sodium hydroxide solution and dilute to about 950 ml. When cool, add the azide solution with stirring and adjust the total volume to 1 litre.

THE RIDEAL - STEWART OR PERMANGANATE MODIFICATION

When ferrous iron in excess of 1 mg per litre, or easily oxidisable organic matter, is present in a sample, the preliminary treatment known as the Rideal - Stewart or permanganate modification should be followed. This treatment also removes nitrites. It should be noted that 1 mg of ferrous iron per litre causes the dissolved oxygen value to be 0·14 mg per litre too low if the unmodified Winkler method is used.

Whereas ferrous salts, should their removal be neglected, will cause an apparent loss of dissolved oxygen, ferric salts may cause an unduly high result to be obtained, owing to release of iodine from iodides in the final acidification stage, especially on long standing. . . . . .

When samples contain drainage from mines, acid stream water or other waters that might contain considerable amounts of ferrous and ferric salts, the permanganate modification together with the potassium fluoride treatment should be followed.

The Rideal - Stewart modification is inappropriate for samples of sulphite wastes . . . . . , or for samples containing heavy suspensions of mud or activated sludge, and should therefore not be used in these cases.

REAGENTS (for the Rideal - Stewart preliminary treatment)—

Potassium permanganate solution, approximately N/8—Dissolve 3·95 g of potassium permanganate in 1 litre of distilled water.

Potassium oxalate solution—Dissolve 2 g of potassium oxalate, $(COOK)_2.H_2O$, in 100 ml of distilled water.

PROCEDURE—

Add exactly 0·7 ml of sulphuric acid, sp.gr. 1·84, to the sample, and follow with sufficient potassium permanganate solution so that, after being well mixed, the liquid retains a definite red-violet tinge for 20 minutes. With unknown samples, the correct amount may have to be ascertained by trial beforehand with another portion of sample, or by adding 1 ml of potassium permanganate solution to the bottle and observing its reaction. If noticeable fading takes place, another 1 ml must be added. If more than 2 ml are required, then a stronger solution should be used. With normal samples, 1 ml is usually sufficient.

After the 20-minute oxidation period has elapsed, remove the excess of permanganate by reaction with oxalate, using not more than the minimum amount of oxalate, since excess leads to results that are lower than the true value. Add 0·5 ml of potassium oxalate solution first, and if the permanganate colour persists after 5 to 10 minutes, add another 0·5 ml, leaving the bottles until complete decolorisation has taken place, otherwise the traces of manganic compounds remaining will react later with the iodides, to give falsely high results. The length of time for the decolorisation to be completed is noticeably dependent on the temperature; . . . . .

It has been pointed out[46] that if iron salts greater in amount than 1 mg per litre are present, then the decolorisation should be allowed to proceed in the dark, because, in the presence of oxalates, light easily reduces ferric salts to the ferrous condition.

When the contents of the bottle are completely decolorised, add 1 ml of manganous sulphate solution, followed by 3 ml of alkaline iodide solution (see p. 28). Well mix the contents of the bottle by inversion and rotation, and proceed as described for the Winkler method. The small error in the calculation given for the Winkler test (due to the displacement of sample by reagents) will be greater in the present case, but can, if desired, be allowed for by the correction given at the top of p. 30. The error due to dissolved oxygen present in the added reagents will again be negligibly small.

When the iron content of the sample is greater than about 10 mg per litre, interaction between ferric salts and iodide may introduce an error. This may be avoided by carrying out the final acidification with 4 ml of 85 per cent. phosphoric acid; alternatively, 2 ml of a 40 per cent. solution of potassium fluoride can be added to the sample at any stage before final acidification.

SPECIAL PROCEDURES

POLYTHIONATE, THIOSULPHATE AND SULPHITE WASTES—

It has been stated that, when the interfering substances present include poly-thionates, thiosulphates or sulphites, permanganate treatment is inadvisable, as it cannot be relied upon to transform these compounds completely into sulphates, and unless this is done, substances will still be present that will interfere with the Winkler procedure. A method of dealing with such samples by preliminary oxidation with alkaline hypochlorite, and subsequent removal of excess of chlorine by means of sulphurous acid, has been suggested.[47] The latter part of this treatment is specified for samples containing residual chlorine, which of course must be removed before the Winkler procedure is undertaken.

Probably in any case of this sort, however, research would be necessary to establish the validity of the method, with use of, for example, the gasometric method of determination as a reference.

SLUDGES AND MUDS—

The suspended matter of **trade effluents**, sludge or river mud, when present in amounts sufficient to give an apparent immediate oxygen demand, prevents the Winkler procedure from giving a true result. In such cases the following preliminary treatment is necessary. Collect a sample of about 1 litre in a glass-stoppered bottle, with the usual precautions against aeration. Add 10 ml of a 10 per cent. solution of aluminium potassium sulphate, and follow with 1 to 2 ml of ammonium hydroxide, sp.gr. 0·880. Re-stopper the bottle and rotate it for about 1 minute. After the floc has settled for about 10 minutes, siphon the clear supernatant liquid into **the reaction bottle, taking the usual precautions to ensure at least two displacements of liquid, and follow the appropriate modification of the Winkler procedure.**[48]

ACTIVATED-SLUDGE MIXED LIQUORS—

If it is desired to determine the dissolved oxygen present in a liquid containing large amounts of easily oxidisable organic matter, as, for example, that flowing from the aeration tanks and channels of an activated-sludge plant or a bio-aeration plant, the direct procedure cannot be employed, because the suspended matter rapidly removes oxygen from solution as it settles. The bottles in which the sample is taken must therefore contain some inhibiting reagent that stops de-oxygenation at the moment of sampling. Ruchhoft and Placak[49] propose an inhibiting reagent of sulphamic acid, copper sulphate and acetic acid, prepared as follows. Dissolve 32 g of sulphamic acid in 475 ml of distilled water and add a solution of 50 g of copper sulphate, $CuSO_4.5H_2O$, in 500 ml of distilled water and 25 ml of glacial acetic acid. Heat should not be used to dissolve the sulphamic acid, nor should the mixed reagent be exposed to heat at any time.

For each 100 ml of sample to be taken, measure 1 ml of this reagent into the sampling bottle, then fill the bottle to overflowing and insert the stopper. Thoroughly mix the contents, allow settlement of sludge to take place, and then siphon the top liquid into a dissolved-oxygen bottle. Then use the sodium azide modification of the Winkler method, as previously described.

EXPRESSION OF RESULTS—

Dissolved oxygen is reported as milligrams per litre. If the result is required as ml of oxygen gas (at 0° C and 760 mm pressure) per litre of sample, the figure representing milligrams per litre of dissolved oxygen must be multiplied by 0·70.

In addition, it is customary and helpful to give the percentage saturation of the sample. For this, reference must be made to the Table of solubility data (Table III), which sets out the solubility of oxygen in fresh water, in mixtures of fresh water and sea water, and in sea water of stated degrees of salinity at various temperatures when in equilibrium with air containing 20·9 per cent. of oxygen under a pressure of 760 mm.

It should be noted that values appreciably in excess of 100 per cent. saturation are sometimes obtained, particularly with samples drawn from localities where oxygen-forming plants (e.g., algae) are flourishing.

Oxygen is less soluble in salt water than in fresh water, and when it is desired to calculate the percentage saturation of oxygen in a sample of **saline liquid**, for example, the salinity of the sample must be known.

TABLE III

OXYGEN SOLUBILITY

Temperature, ° C	Solubility of oxygen in water in equilibrium with air at 760 mm, mg per litre	Correction to be subtracted for each degree of salinity, g of total salts per 1000 g **of saline water**
0	14·16	0·08405
1	13·77	0·08153
2	13·40	0·07908
3	13·05	0·07671
4	12·70	0·07440
5	12·37	0·07218
6	12·06	0·07002
7	11·76	0·06795
8	11·47	0·06595
9	11·19	0·06402
10	10·92	0·06217
11	10·67	0·06039
12	10·43	0·05869
13	10·20	0·05706
14	9·98	0·05551
15	9·76	0·05404
16	9·56	0·05263
17	9·37	0·05130
18	9·18	0·05005
19	9·01	0·04887
20	8·84	0·04777
21	8·68	0·04674
22	8·53	0·04579
23	8·38	0·04491
24	8·25	0·04410
25	8·11	0·04338
26	7·99	0·04272
27	7·86	0·04214
28	7·75	0·04164
29	7·64	0·04121
30	7·53	0·04085

THE SOLUBILITY OF OXYGEN IN WATER

The solubility of oxygen in water has been investigated by the Water Pollution Research Laboratory,[50] who have obtained figures up to 4 per cent. lower than previously accepted values. Their results are related by the empirical equation—

$$C_o = 14 \cdot 161 - 0 \cdot 3943T + 0 \cdot 007714T^2 - 0 \cdot 0000646T^3,$$

where C_o is the saturation concentration of oxygen in mg per litre at temperature $T° C$. The formula applies to water in equilibrium with air at a pressure of 760 mm and containing 20·9 per cent. of oxygen.

The effect of salinity on the solubility of oxygen was also investigated and the following formula accounted for the results—

$$C_s = C_o - S(0 \cdot 0841 - 0 \cdot 00256T + 0 \cdot 0000374T^2),$$

where C_s is the solubility at a salinity S (g of total salts per 1000 g of saline water) at temperature $T° C$.

The results were consistent with the commonly accepted assumption that the solubility at a given temperature varies lineally with the salinity.

The Table of solubility data (Table III), has been calculated from the above equations and is recommended for general use. The first column gives the temperature, the second the solubility in water containing no salts and the third a correction factor, to be subtracted from the solubility, to obtain the figure appropriate to water of salinity 1 g per 1000 g. For other salinities a proportionate correction factor should be used.

An exact correction for salinity can only be made for solutions containing inorganic salts of the same composition and in the same relative concentrations as are found in sea water, since the solubility of oxygen in solutions containing other salts, or the same salts in different proportional concentrations, has not been determined. In cases when the correction does apply, for example to estuary waters, the salinity is determined by the standard international method.[51]

EFFECT OF ORDINARY VARIATIONS IN BAROMETRIC PRESSURE ON CONCENTRATION OF DISSOLVED OXYGEN—

If the barometric pressure at the time of sampling is not 760 mm, then the saturation values at the actual pressure will vary slightly from those given in Table III, according to the formula—

$$S_x = \frac{SP_x}{760},$$

where S_x is the solubility at pressure P_x, S is the solubility at 760 mm, and P_x is the observed pressure in mm.

Most ordinary observations of barometric pressure at sea level in the British Isles fall within the range of 760 ± 20 mm. The following Table shows the variation in solubility over this range—

Temperature, °C	Concentration of dissolved oxygen in equilibrium at 760 mm, mg per litre	Assumed variation in barometric pressure		Variation in concentration in dissolved oxygen, mg per litre
		mm	%	
10	10·92			± 0·29
20	8·84	± 20	± 2·63	± 0·23
30	7·53			± 0·20

The total variation (*i.e.*, twice the variation from the mean) would be easily detectable in accurate measurements and might be large enough to have an influence on observations in the field.

EFFECT OF HEIGHT ABOVE SEA LEVEL ON CONCENTRATION OF DISSOLVED OXYGEN—

If the temperature of the atmosphere at different heights above sea level be taken as constant, it can be shown that for a gas that obeys Boyle's law the relation between the altitude, A, and the barometric height, H, in relation to the barometric height, H_0, at sea level is given by—

$$A = K \log \frac{H_0}{H}.$$

For measurements of A in feet, logarithms to the base 10 and a temperature of $0°$ C, $K = 60,370$. The following table gives some values calculated from this formula—

EFFECT OF ALTITUDE ON BAROMETRIC PRESSURE

Altitude, feet	1000	5000	10,000	16,404 (= 5000 metres)
Calculated barometric pressure,	731	628	519	408

Since the temperature of the atmosphere is not in fact constant at all altitudes, the above relationship is not exactly obeyed. In one particular year, however, the observed mean barometric pressure at an altitude over the British Isles of 5000 metres was reported as 403 mm, compared with the calculated 408 mm, indicating that deviations up to that height were not large.

In the British Isles it may be assumed that few . . . . . works or polluted rivers are at a height above sea level of more than 1000 feet, and the taking of this and the normal pressure variations into account might diminish the figures (Table III) by up to 6 per cent. or increase them by up to 3 per cent. Only rarely would this make an important difference to the value of percentage saturation. It might, however, be worth while introducing a permanent correction for height for regular sampling points more than 500 feet above sea level.

At heights greater than 1000 feet such a correction becomes essential.

Biochemical Oxygen Demand (B.O.D.)*

When polluting organic matter is discharged into a watercourse or lake, a natural purifying action tends to set in, owing to the action of certain micro-organisms, which utilise the . . . . . oxygen dissolved in the water to oxidise the polluting substances. The length of time required for complete purification depends upon many conditions, including temperature and the nature of the organic matter.

The Royal Commission on Sewage Disposal, with which the names of Adeney, Letts, McGowan and Frye are widely associated, proposed that the weight of dissolved oxygen required by a definite volume of liquid for the process of biochemical oxidation during 5 days at 65° F be taken as a measure of the quality of the liquid. This test was first known as the "Dissolved Oxygen Absorption Test" or the "Royal Commission Test"; of late years "Biochemical Oxygen Demand" has superseded the early names, and now the abbreviation "B.O.D." has become almost universal.

The "Dilution Method" of determining B.O.D. is the one most generally used and the details of this, as specified in the Ministry of Housing and Local Government's booklet on Methods of Chemical Analysis as Applied to Sewage and Sewage Effluents, are quoted in the following paragraphs. Another procedure is the "Manometric Method," which has, up to the present, been used mainly for research, but which has many advantages and may well prove to be useful for works control. A following section deals with the general principles of this test, but for working details of the procedure to be adopted readers are referred to the original literature on the subject, for which references are given.

* See footnote, p. 27.

THE DILUTION METHOD

The principle of the test is simple. The dissolved-oxygen content of the liquid, with or without dilution, is determined before and after incubation for 5 days at the standard temperature, the difference giving the oxygen demand of the sample, allowance being made for the dilution, if any, that the sample received.

In practice, several points must be watched carefully in order to obtain concordant results.

Preservatives must not be added to samples intended for the determination of biochemical oxygen demand. So far as is possible the B.O.D. test should be proceeded with directly the sample is available; if kept at ordinary room temperature for several hours, a very appreciable change may occur in the B.O.D., depending on the character of the sample. In some instances it may decrease and in others it may increase. The decrease at room temperature has in a few cases been found to be as much as 40 per cent. during the first 8 hours of storage.

If samples cannot be dealt with at once for the determination of B.O.D., they should wherever practicable be stored at about 5° C. In the case of a composite sample representing a 24-hour (or other long-period) flow it is desirable to keep all the individual hourly samples at about 5° C until the composite sample can be made up for the B.O.D. determination.[52]

It is necessary that excess of dissolved oxygen be present during the whole period of incubation and desirable that at least **30 per cent.** of the saturation value remains after 5 days. Since only about 9 mg of dissolved oxygen per litre can be present in a saturated water at the temperature of incubation, it follows that samples that absorb more than about 5 mg per litre during incubation for 5 days require more oxygen than they can themselves dissolve. This is the case with . . . . . many waste liquids and . . . . . polluted river waters. The additional oxygen is supplied by diluting the sample with clean well aerated water, the amount of dilution depending upon the nature of the sample.

DILUTION WATER—

There has been much controversy about the nature of the water to be used for dilution, and the subject has been investigated at length. The logical diluent for an . . . . . effluent would appear to be the river water into which it is discharged, but this method could be adopted only in special cases, and obviously breaks down when effluents from widely differing localities are dealt with in one laboratory. Moreover, the river water may itself have a considerable oxygen demand.

Distilled water alone is unsatisfactory. In this country many laboratories have used tap water that has been well aerated and stored for some time at the incubator temperature. As tap waters differ very much in their content of inorganic salts, and as most of them are now chlorinated, it is recommended that a synthetic dilution water be employed, particularly for determinations the results of which might be required as evidence in a court of law. For less vital determinations a well aerated and stored tap water could continue to be employed, preferably after it has been established that the results were generally comparable with those given with the synthetic dilution water now to be described.

The synthetic dilution water recommended[53] is prepared by adding small quantities of four solutions to good quality distilled water. The latter should be prepared from stills of block tin, **hard-glass** or cast iron with a condenser of **hard-glass**, stainless steel, block tin or other suitable material. Copper stills **or condensers** should not be used, for the water must contain less than 0·01 mg of copper per litre, which otherwise would exert an inhibitory action on the biochemical processes. The distilled water is aerated at the temperature of incubation to remove excess of carbon dioxide and to saturate the water with air. Water approximating to distilled water in composition may now be cheaply prepared by ion-exchange methods, but little experience is yet available in this country on the suitability of such water as a diluent in the B.O.D. test, and more work on the subject is clearly desirable. In its absence the general use of such water cannot be recommended: it has been stated that it can prove unsuitable.

The following stock solutions are required—

Ferric chloride solution—Dissolve 0·25 g of ferric chloride, $FeCl_3.6H_2O$, in 1 litre of distilled water.

Calcium chloride solution—Dissolve 11·0 g of calcium chloride (or the equivalent if the hydrate is used) in 1 litre of distilled water.

Magnesium sulphate solution—Dissolve 10·0 g of magnesium sulphate, $MgSO_4.7H_2O$, in 1 litre of distilled water.

Phosphate buffer stock solution—Dissolve 34 g of potassium dihydrogen phosphate in 500 ml of distilled water. Add 175 ml of N sodium hydroxide. This should give a solution of pH 7·2. Add 1·5 g of ammonium sulphate and dilute to 1 litre.

The dilution water is prepared with freshly distilled water, which should be collected in a vessel previously cleaned with chromic acid mixture and well washed. To each litre of distilled water are added 0·5 ml of ferric chloride solution, 2·5 ml of calcium chloride solution, 2·5 ml of magnesium sulphate solution and 1·25 ml of phosphate buffer stock solution. The water should then be well aerated, stored at the incubation temperature and used as soon as possible. Any remaining unused after 1 week should be discarded and the bottle cleaned with chromic acid mixture and well washed. Stocks of dilution water should never be "topped up" with fresh solution.

These precautions in the use of standard dilution water are necessary, because it has been observed that, if kept over a long period, nitrification takes place and, if the water is then used for the B.O.D. test, an inaccurate value is obtained.

It has also been stated that, when dilution water is incubated alone under standard conditions, it should not absorb more than 0·2 mg of oxygen per litre. Cases have, however, occurred when substantially higher figures have been obtained for no apparent reason. It is desirable, therefore, to use as little dilution water as possible consistent with (a) at least 30 per cent. of the dissolved oxygen being present at the end of the test and (b) the actual dilution being below the bacteriostatic level. With river waters, it may not always be necessary to use dilution water.

BOTTLES—

It is recommended that narrow-mouthed glass-stoppered bottles of a nominal capacity of 250 ml be used for the determination of B.O.D., as for the determination of dissolved oxygen, and that they be cleaned in the same way with chromic acid mixture.

Some analysts, especially those who have to deal regularly with a very large number of samples, prefer to use bottles of about 125 ml capacity, thus reducing the incubator space required. There is reason to believe, however, that with some types of samples the size of bottles (*i.e.*, the ratio of the glass surface to the volume of liquid) may have some influence on the result obtained. The analyst wishing to use small bottles must therefore satisfy himself that such procedure gives the same results as with the use of standard-size bottles. In all determinations in connection with disputes or disagreements standard-size bottles should be used.

D

TEMPERATURE—

To conform with international practice, it is recommended that the temperature of incubation for the B.O.D. test be 20° C. A water bath, or water-cooled incubator, or constant-temperature room, thermostatically controlled, is usually employed for carrying out the test. The limit of error of the temperature should be ± 0·5° C.

INCUBATION—

The period of incubation in the standard test is 5 days, which means 120 ± 1 hours.

In special cases, or for research work, other periods of incubation are sometimes selected, usually 1, 2, 10 and 20 days, but 5 days' incubation is always taken for the standard test.

Incubation should be carried out in the dark. Some waters may contain green plants, which, if incubated in the light, would give off oxygen by photosynthesis and thus interfere with the B.O.D. determination. The polluting effect of an effluent on a stream may, of course, be considerably altered by the photosynthesis of green plants present, but it is quite impossible to determine this effect quantitatively in incubation experiments.

PROCEDURE—

Unless the pH value of the sample is within the range 6·5 to 8·2, add sufficient alkali or acid to bring it within that range. The amount of acid or alkali to be added should be determined first on a separate sample.

Some samples of . . . . . trade wastes may be sterile and will need inoculation with fresh micro-organisms before incubation. It is usually recommended, and it is often convenient and satisfactory, to use as an inoculum a fresh sewage effluent of good quality obtained from a settling tank, after an aerobic biological process of purification. If this is done, to each litre of dilution water add 5 ml of the sewage effluent. If necessary, the effluent should be settled in a cylinder (not filtered) until the supernatant liquid contains less than 30 mg of suspended solids per litre and has a B.O.D. not exceeding 20 mg per litre.

The question of the uniform seeding of sterile discharges before incubation is not such a simple matter as might appear, for different sewage effluents may contain different bacterial flora, and even the same effluent may vary from hour to hour and from day to day, and, for some trade wastes, sewage effluent might not be suitable as an inoculum until it has been suitably conditioned.

When the B.O.D. value found by the standard test, with sewage effluent as an inoculum, is substantially less than about two-thirds of the chemical oxygen demand from dichromate, an anomalous behaviour must be suspected. This may arise from one of three causes (i) the sample may contain compounds having molecular structures resistant to biological breakdown, (ii) the constituents of the waste may be amenable to oxidation, but the organisms present in the inoculum are of an unsuitable type or require acclimatisation, and (iii) toxic or bacteriostatic compounds may be present, exerting an inhibiting effect at the concentration employed for the test.

Compounds constitutionally resistant to breakdown are not potentially polluting when the oxygen depletion of the receiving waters is the sole criterion. Substances amenable to breakdown given suitable conditions will, however, generally contribute to the pollution load, for organisms will probably be present in the receiving stream capable of effecting their destruction.

There is no completely satisfactory method of preparing an active inoculum for test purposes. Sewage organisms can, however, often be suitably conditioned by aerating mixtures of settled sewage and waste liquor for periods of 1 to 7 days.

Air should be supplied through a sintered-glass diffuser. It may be necessary to use initially a diluted sample of liquor, the concentration being increased stepwise until the test concentration is reached.

The need for a conditioned seed may be found by determining B.O.D. values for periods longer than 5 days. Frequently a conditioned seed develops during the first few days of incubation with a consequent rise in the rate of oxygen depletion towards the end of the 5-day period. Care should, however, be exercised in differentiating between this increase in rate and that normally resulting from the development of nitrifying activity.

Many trade effluents contain constituents that repress biological oxidation in concentrations higher than well defined threshold values. When this limiting concentration is lower than that prevailing in the B.O.D. test bottle, the sample must be diluted until a maximum value for the B.O.D. on an undiluted basis is obtained.

The advantageous use of the manometric technique for the study of inoculum activity and inhibiting action is described later under "Manometric Methods."

It is possible that some samples may be supersaturated with dissolved oxygen, especially waters in which algal growths are flourishing. Such samples should be well shaken in a partly filled bottle, or suction may be applied to remove excess of gas, if the liquid is to be incubated without dilution. If the sample is to be diluted, then this may be done with partly de-aerated water.

Unless the B.O.D. of the sample is already known approximately, the required degree of dilution will not be known and more than one dilution will have to be set up. A useful guide to the strength of the sample may be obtained by first determining the chemical oxygen demand, either by the 4-hour permanganate test or, better, by the dichromate method. If the general nature of the trade waste is known, an approximate estimate of the order of magnitude of the ratio of biochemical oxygen demand to chemical oxygen demand may be made, and hence a very rough estimate of the expected B.O.D. If the expected B.O.D. is D mg per litre, then 1 volume of sample would require about $D/5$ volumes of dilution water and, when an unknown sample is being examined, this dilution would be set up, with at least one higher and one lower dilution.

Mix the sample and dilution water (containing when necessary the inoculum of sewage effluent) in a graduated cylinder or other suitable vessel. Thorough mixing may be accomplished with the aid of a plunge type of rod without entraining air in the mixture. Violent shaking should be avoided.

For each dilution of the sample, carefully pour the mixture into bottles, one for the initial determination of dissolved oxygen, and one (or two if a duplicate is desired) for incubation, avoiding the entrainment of air. At the same time fill two bottles completely with dilution water, containing, if necessary, an inoculum of sewage effluent. Leave the bottles for 2 to 3 minutes, when, by tapping the neck with a stopper, the few minute bubbles which sometimes form during filling can be displaced. Then firmly insert the stoppers.

Determine immediately the initial concentration of dissolved oxygen in one bottle of the mixture of sample and dilution water, and in one of the bottles containing only dilution water, using, in both cases, the Alsterberg method (see p. 30) or, if necessary, the Rideal - Stewart modification (see p. 31). Place the other bottles (those containing the mixture of sample and dilution water, and that containing the plain dilution water to act as a blank) in an incubator. After incubation at 20° C for 5 days, determine the dissolved oxygen in the diluted samples and the blank.

. . . . .

CALCULATION OF RESULT—

If 100 ml of mixture require x and y ml of $N/80$ sodium thiosulphate before and after incubation, respectively, if the dilution water itself shows no consumption of dissolved oxygen and if a volumes of dilution water were used to one volume of sample, then—

$$\text{B.O.D.} = (x - y)(a + 1) \text{ mg per litre.}$$

If the dilution water consumes oxygen in the 5 days equivalent to z ml of $N/80$ sodium thiosulphate per 100 ml of the water, then the formula becomes—

$$\text{B.O.D.} = \left(x - y - \frac{az}{a + 1} \right) (a + 1) \text{ mg per litre.}$$

The initial dissolved-oxygen content of the mixture to be incubated may also be calculated from the separate dissolved-oxygen contents of the sample and of the dilution water. This method is appropriate for samples having an immediate dissolved-oxygen demand.

It is sometimes convenient to carry out the dilution of samples for B.O.D. determination by adding appropriate volumes of sample directly to bottles of known capacity that already contain sufficient dilution water so that together with the sample the liquid reaches the top of the neck of the bottle. The sample is added carefully by means of a pipette well below the surface of the water, the bottle is stoppered and the contents thoroughly mixed. Another bottle is completely filled with the dilution water at the same time, so that the dissolved oxygen at the start of the test may be calculated. The bottle containing the diluted sample is incubated as before, and the dissolved oxygen is determined after the 5-day period. This method is particularly useful for determining the B.O.D. of samples that have an *immediate* demand for dissolved oxygen. Such a demand is not included in the ordinary method, in which the initial dissolved oxygen content is found after the sample has been diluted in a cylinder and then poured into bottles.

In this case calculation is a little more difficult and an example is given.

A 2·5-ml portion of **sample** was added at the bottom of a 260-ml bottle filled with dilution water. After 5 days at 20° C, 100 ml required 4·1 ml of $N/80$ sodium thiosulphate; 100 ml of the dilution water used required 8·9 ml of $N/80$ sodium thiosulphate before incubation and 8·8 ml after incubation.

Since 260 ml of mixture contained 2·5 ml of **sample**, 100 ml of mixture contained 99·0 ml of dilution water, which had an initial dissolved-oxygen equivalent to $8·9 \times 0·99 = 8·81$ ml of $N/80$ sodium thiosulphate. The oxygen demand of this volume of dilution water was equivalent to 0·1 ml of $N/80$ sodium thiosulphate and hence the initial dissolved-oxygen content of 100 ml of mixture may be regarded as equivalent to 8·7 ml of $N/80$ sodium thiosulphate.

The oxygen consumed by the **sample** in 100 ml was equivalent to $8·7 - 4·1 = 4·6$ ml of $N/80$ sodium thiosulphate.

Therefore, B.O.D. of **sample**, mg per litre $= 4·6 \times$ dilution

$$= \frac{4·6 \times 260}{2·5} = 480 \text{ mg per litre.}$$

When the dilution is small, an appreciable error may be introduced if it is assumed, as in the above example, that the sample contains no dissolved oxygen. The method has its chief value, however, when large dilutions are required, in which cases the sample itself is unlikely to contain much oxygen, and when there is an immediate oxygen demand, in which case the sample is unlikely to contain any oxygen at all.

Dilutions sensibly greater than 1 in 100, such as may be needed for . . . . . some trade wastes, should be made by diluting the sample first in a calibrated flask or measure, and then adding the appropriate amount of this dilution to the incubation bottles containing the final dilution water. . . . . .

Coarse suspended matter in some **trade effluents** may cause difficulty, since the distribution of the solids may be uneven when the sample is made up into dilutions. Apart from the appearance of the sample, this unevenness may be shown by discrepancies in the results from different dilutions or duplicate dilutions. In these cases some means of disintegration and dispersion of suspended matter is needed in order to give a certain minimum degree of homogeneity to the sample. Since there is little doubt that artificial disintegration of solid matter leads to a higher oxygen demand than would otherwise be measured, and since the problem described does not normally arise, such processing of samples cannot be advocated in general. Moreover, there is no simple procedure capable of easy standardisation. In those cases in which dispersion of solids is necessary, however, an attempt should be made to use a method that gives a reproducible degree of disintegration.

CHLORINATED EFFLUENTS—

Some . . . . . trade wastes contain either residual chlorine or the products resulting from the action of chlorine on certain constituents. Such liquids cannot be used as received for the determination of B.O.D. because of the bactericidal effect of the chlorine or of its products, and also because the chlorine would introduce an error into the determination of dissolved oxygen.

If the sample gives a positive reaction with neutral starch - iodide, this normally indicates the presence of chlorine or chlorinated compounds. These substances may be removed by treating a portion of the sample with the calculated amount of sodium bisulphite, so that there remains in the liquid neither chlorine nor sulphite; this treated portion may then be used for the B.O.D. test after inoculation with suitable micro-organisms, as described in a previous section.

If a positive result is obtained, it is probable that this procedure will give reasonably good results . . . . . , but in the case of other effluents . . . . . it is possible that the chlorine will have combined with organic compounds present, producing substances that, although giving no test for chlorine with starch - iodide, are inhibitory to biochemical oxidation processes or are even bactericidal. It must be admitted that the B.O.D. as determined by this technique is generally lower than would be expected, having regard to the organic content as measured by other tests.

There is a lack of knowledge on the effect of chlorination on many compounds, which also adds to the difficulty of determining the actual oxygen-absorbing capacity of samples containing such substances.

Should it be desirable to obtain a figure for B.O.D. of a chlorinated effluent, notwithstanding the uncertainty of the interpretation of the test in these circumstances, the following procedure should be used. Add a crystal or two of potassium iodide to a convenient volume of sample, depending on the concentration of residual chlorine, and titrate the liquid with a solution of sodium bisulphite, using a few drops of fresh starch indicator solution. If the sample is alkaline to phenolphthalein, bring it to the acid side of this indicator (*i.e.*, to a pH value of about 7·0) by the addition of dilute sulphuric acid, before titration of the chlorine. Approximately $N/80$ is a convenient concentration of bisulphite solution to use, or $N/40$ for samples containing heavy doses of chlorine. To discharge the residual chlorine in 1 litre of sample containing for example 2 mg per litre the addition of 4·5 ml of $N/80$ sodium bisulphite is required.

To another portion of sample, sufficient to carry out the B.O.D. test, add the requisite amount of dilute sulphuric acid (when necessary), followed by the calculated volume of sodium bisulphite solution as determined by the previous titration.   After thoroughly mixing, set aside for several minutes, then check the absence of chlorine by testing a small portion of the treated sample with neutral starch - iodide; likewise check the absence of excess of bisulphite in another portion by means of starch indicator solution and a drop of $N/80$ iodine solution, which should develop a blue colour.

Make up the dilutions with inoculated water and proceed as for unchlorinated samples.

SLUDGES AND MUDS—

The assessment of the B.O.D. of samples of sludges and muds requires a special procedure.   The degree of dilution will naturally depend on the nature of the sludge or mud and, unless there is definite guidance from previous experience, several dilutions will have to be set up.

The determination of the initial dissolved oxygen of the dilution, and of the final dissolved oxygen after incubation, **may** be carried out after the liquid has been clarified, **if necessary**, by the charcoal and aluminium hydroxide procedure described under "Nitrogen Present as Nitrite," ("alum flocculation").

It should be borne in mind that mud may have an immediate oxygen demand.[54]

During the incubation period, the solid matter must be kept in suspension and not allowed to remain at the bottom of the bottle all the time.   This requires the use of some device to ensure that the bottles are kept in slow rotation and inversion.

MANOMETRIC METHODS*

One of the disadvantages of using the standard method for determining the B.O.D. of industrial wastes, particularly those containing a substantial concentration of organic matter, is that, because of the low solubility of oxygen in water, the waste may have to be diluted with a very high proportion of water to provide sufficient oxygen to give a result in the test.   Also the single value for oxygen absorbed in 5 days gives no indication of changes in rate of up-take of oxygen during the period of incubation, or of the possible effects of inhibiting substances, lack of adequate nutrients or lack of acclimatised seeding organisms.   These factors can be studied to a limited extent by setting up large numbers of dilutions under different conditions, but, when they are likely to be of importance, a more satisfactory method is to observe directly in a respirometer the up-take of oxygen by the sample from an atmosphere of air or oxygen.   In such an apparatus, either the undiluted trade waste, or any desired dilution, can be studied and the progress of absorption of oxygen by a single sample can be continuously followed.

Respirometers were originally devised for studying the respiration of biological tissues, but are suitable for the examination of any system in which a gaseous reactant is evolved or absorbed over a period of hours or days with a consequent change in pressure or volume of the gaseous phase.   For the purpose of studying biochemical reactions in which oxygen is absorbed and carbon dioxide produced, the respirometer consists essentially of an absorption flask in which the sample to be studied is placed and in which there is a separate section for holding potassium hydroxide solution for absorption of carbon dioxide.   The flask is connected to a manometer and the free space above the sample is filled with a known volume of air or oxygen.   Multiple units are normally used and are mounted on a frame so that the whole can be mechanically shaken with the flasks immersed in a constant-temperature water bath.   Several different systems are used for measuring the change in volume or pressure of the gaseous phase.   The pressure of the gas can be brought to a constant value at each reading and the change in volume observed, or the change in pressure in relation to a compensating flask may be used to calculate the change in volume, as

* This section has been prepared by the Joint A.B.C.M. - S.A.C. Committee, and is *not* taken from the Ministry of Housing and Local Government's handbook (see footnote, p. 27).

in the Barcroft differential respirometer; or the gas may be brought to constant volume and the change in pressure observed, allowance being made for changes in barometric pressure, as in the Warburg respirometer. For details of design, calibration and use of respirometers, the original literature should be consulted.[55],[56],[57] The Warburg type is the simplest from the point of view of calculation of the results and is probably the most widely used in the British Isles. In the respirometers mentioned the volume of sample is usually about 3 ml, but with suitable flasks, volumes up to 50 ml may be used.[58] For much larger samples (up to 750 ml) a differential apparatus with internal stirring instead of mechanical shaking may be used.[59] In using a respirometer, it is essential that the size and nature of sample taken, and the degree of shaking or stirring, should be such that the rate of transfer of oxygen from the gaseous to the liquid phase should be considerably greater than the rate of utilisation of oxygen, as otherwise false results will be obtained.

When substances inhibitory to biological action are present in an industrial waste, it is generally found, when the waste is diluted, that there is a critical concentration below which the inhibitory action becomes negligible. By setting up a number of different dilutions in a series of respirometers and plotting the rate of up-take of oxygen in each case, the minimum dilution required to achieve the maximum B.O.D. can be found and can be used as a guide to the minimum dilution that could be used in the standard B.O.D. test to obtain reliable results.

In a similar manner the effect of addition of compounds of nutrient elements, for example, nitrogen, phosphorus and potassium, on the rate and degree of up-take of oxygen in biological oxidation of a trade waste can be studied.

In the standard dilution test for B.O.D. it is specified that samples of trade waste likely to be sterile should be seeded by adding a small proportion of sewage effluent containing a mixed flora of micro-organisms. In respirometer experiments seeding of sterile samples is also necessary. The inoculum may not be suitable for biological oxidation of the trade waste, but may be amenable to adaptation or acclimatisation to produce a flora that will bring about oxidation. In this case determination of the B.O.D. by the standard dilution technique would give false and probably non-reproducible results, but a curve of oxygen absorption against time, plotted from the results of a respirometer experiment, would show a lag period during which little or no oxygen was absorbed, followed by a rising curve of oxygen absorption when the flora had become adapted to the new conditions. If liquid from the respirometer reaction flask were then used to inoculate a further sample of trade waste in a second experiment, the lag period might be shortened or might disappear.[60] When, by successive inoculations, the lag period had been eliminated, a normal oxygen up-take curve would be obtained, giving a result for the B.O.D. more in accord with conditions of oxidation that would obtain in a biological treatment plant, or in a river into which a trade waste was being continuously discharged.

When applied to domestic sewage, the biochemical oxygen demand measured by the manometric method has been stated to be higher by 15 per cent.[56],[61] or more[62] than the value obtained by the standard dilution technique. In recent experiments at the Water Pollution Research Laboratory, however, results obtained by the two methods have been found to be in good agreement. When applied to an industrial waste, the result may be higher or lower than that obtained by the dilution method.[56] It is not certain, therefore, whether the manometric method could be put forward as an alternative to the standard dilution method, but it is recommended for studying and rectifying conditions that may invalidate the dilution test if applied indiscriminately to trade wastes. Although the manometric technique is no simpler than the dilution technique, under the right conditions it might possibly be used to obtain an indication of the biological oxidisability of a trade waste in a shorter period of test than 5 days.

GENERAL OBSERVATIONS*

In assessing the B.O.D. of various types of waste waters, it is often desirable to draw the oxidation curve of the sample, *i.e.*, to plot a graph of the absorption of oxygen against time during the incubation period, **as described under "Manometric Methods."** Such a graph will reveal whether the liquid contained immediately oxidisable substances, and also whether there was any departure from the logarithmic curve given by a pseudo-unimolecular reaction. For example, nitrification during incubation would cause such a departure.

The subject of nitrification of samples during incubation in the test for B.O.D. in 5 days has caused some controversy in recent years. The oxidation of carbon-aceous matter to carbon dioxide, and of nitrogenous matter and ammonia to nitrates, are separate processes, and it is thought by some that the oxygen requirements of the former only should be included in the oxygen demand, and that the inclusion of the latter leads to unfairly high results when the effect of the liquid on a stream is considered.

It is probable that in the determination of the B.O.D. in 5 days of crude and settled sewages, and of the majority of industrial wastes, nitrification is not important, but it may easily be a serious factor in the oxygen demands of purified . . . . . effluents, especially those that have received a high degree of treatment. In such cases it is very likely that nitrification sets in shortly after incubation has begun and proceeds simultaneously with carbonaceous oxidation. . . . . .

Attempts have been made to suppress nitrification during incubation, but so far a completely successful method has not been developed, since carbonaceous oxidation tends to be suppressed by substances that suppress nitrification.

There has been much discussion as to whether the oxygen absorbed by nitro-genous compounds in an effluent should properly be included in the value for B.O.D. in 5 days as reported. It is recommended that in the present state of knowledge the oxygen demand due to nitrification processes should be included in the value given and, if, in special investigations, nitrification is suppressed during incubation, this should be clearly stated when reporting the results. If proof exists that nitrifica-tion is responsible for a substantial up-take of oxygen during incubation, this also should be stated: it must then be shown that the content of nitrogen in the form of nitrite plus nitrate in the liquid after incubation was greater than in the corres-ponding liquid before incubation.

During the last 25 or 30 years, the test for B.O.D. in 5 days has been universally adopted as one important measure of the quality of a liquid containing **biologically oxidisable organic matter. The warning should be repeated, however, that particularly in regard to its application to trade effluents the test is by no means infallible; the results should always be considered in conjunction with the results of other determinations. Mention should also be made of the fact that salinity may have an effect on the figure obtained for B.O.D.**[20]

REFERENCES

1. Adeney, W. E., and Dawson, B. B., *Sci. Proc. Roy. Dublin Soc.*, 1926, **18**, 199.
2. American Public Health Association, "Standard Methods for the Examination of Water, Sewage and Industrial Wastes," Tenth Edition, New York, 1955, p. 332.
3. Heukelekian, H., *Sewage Wks J.*, 1947, **19**, 612.
4. Sawyer, C. N., Callejas, P., Moore, M., and Tom, A. Q. Y., *Sewage Ind. Wastes*, 1950, **22**, 26.
5. U.S. Federation of Sewage and Industrial Wastes Association, Research Committee, Sub-Committee on Toxicity of Industrial Wastes, Section II, *Sewage Ind. Wastes*, 1954, **26**, 536.
6. Ingols, R. S., and Kirkpatrick, E. S., *Anal. Chem.*, 1952, **24**, 1881.

* From the Ministry of Housing and Local Government's handbook, with changes (see footnote, p. 27).

7. Placak, O. R., Ruchhoft, C. C., and Snapp, R. G., *Ind. Eng. Chem.*, 1949, **41**, 2238.
8. Southgate, B. A., *J. Soc. Chem. Ind.*, 1933, **52**, 1τ.
9. Ludzack, F. J., Moore, W. A., Krieger, H. L., and Ruchhoft, C. C., *Sewage Ind. Wastes*, 1951, **23**, 1298.
10. Gotaas, H. B., *Sewage Wks J.*, 1949, **21**, 818.
11. Grindley, J., and Wheatland, A. B., *Wat. Sanit. Eng.*, 1956, **6**, 10.
12. Bogan, R. H., and Sawyer, C. N., *Sewage Ind. Wastes*, 1954, **26**, 1069; 1955, **27**, 917; *Proc. 10th Ind. Waste Conf.*, in *Purdue Univ. Eng. Bull., Ext. Ser., No. 89*, 1955, 231.
13. Hammerton, C., *J. Appl. Chem.*, 1955, **5**, 517.
14. Sawyer, C. N., Bogan, R. H., and Simpson, J. R., *Ind. Eng. Chem.*, 1956, **48**, 236.
15. Sheets, W. D., and Malaney, G. W., *Ohio State Univ. Studies, Eng. Exp. Sta. Bull. No. 157*, 1955, **24**, No. 3, 1.
16. Heukelekian, H., and Rand, M. C., *Sewage Ind. Wastes*, 1955, **27**, 1040.
17. Lamb, C. B., and Jenkins, G. F., *Proc. 7th Ind. Waste Conf.*, in *Purdue Univ. Eng. Bull., Ext. Ser., No. 79*, 1952, 326.
18. Lyon, H. D., *Chem. Eng. Progr.*, 1950, **46**, 388.
19. Mills, E. J., and Stack, V. T., *Proc. 8th Ind. Waste Conf.*, in *Purdue Univ. Eng. Bull., Ext. Ser., No. 83*, 1953, 492.
20. Sierp, F., Committee on Sewage Chemistry, *Berichte der Abwassertechnischen Vereinigung e. V.* (Volume 4, *Die Wiesbadener Tagung*, 1952), R. Oldenbourg, Munich, 1953, p. 132.
21. Stafford, W., and Northrup, H. J., *Proc. Amer. Ass. Text. Chem. & Col.*, 1955, 355.
22. Gellman, I., Thesis, "Direct Oxygen Utilisation Method and its Applications to Study of Oxidation Characteristics of Wastes," Rutgers University, N.J., 1952.
23. Heukelekian, H., *Sewage Wks J.*, 1947, **19**, 875.
24. Abbott, W. E., and Fearn, R. J., *Sewage Ind. Wastes*, 1951, **23**, 505.
25. Tyler, R. G., and Gunter, S., *Sewage Wks J.*, 1948, **20**, 709.
26. Abbott, W. A., *Ind. Eng. Chem.*, 1927, **19**, 919.
27. Ingols, R. S., and Murray, P. E., *Wat. & Sewage Wks*, 1948, **95**, 112.
28. Moore, W. A., Kroner, R. C., and Ruchhoft, C. C., *Anal. Chem.*, 1949, **21**, 953.
29. Moore, W. A., Ludzack, F. J., and Ruchhoft, C. C., *Ibid.*, 1951, **23**, 1297.
30. Moore, W. A., and Walker, W. W., *Ibid.*, 1956, **28**, 164.
31. Roberts, H. V., and Sanderson, W. W., *Sewage Ind. Wastes*, 1953, **25**, 793.
32. Muers, M. M., *J. Soc. Chem. Ind.*, 1936, **55**, 71τ.
33. Lovett, M., and Garner, J. H., *J. Inst. Sewage Purif.*, 1935, II, 283.
34. Cameron, W. M., and Moore, T. B., *Analyst*, 1957, **82**, 677.
35. Cameron, W. M., *J. Inst. Sewage Purif.*, 1944, 204.
36. Jenkins, S. H., and Hewitt, C. H., *Ibid.*, 1944, 204.
37. Roberts, R. F., *Analyst*, 1955, **80**, 517.
38. Lovett, M., and Garner, J. H., *J. Inst. Sewage Purif.*, 1935, II, 283.
39. Winkler, L. W., *Ber.*, 1888, **21**, 2843.
40. Alsterberg, G., *Biochem. Z.*, 1925, **159**, 36.
41. Rideal, S., and Stewart, G. G., *Analyst*, 1901, **26**, 141.
42. Adams, R. C., Barnett, R. E., and Keller, D. E., *Proc. Amer. Soc. Test Mater.*, 1943, **43**, 1252.
43. White, A. H., Leland, C. H., and Button, D. W., *Ibid.*, 1939, **36**, 707.
44. "Methods of Testing Water Used in Industry," B.S. 2960: 1956.
45. American Public Health Association, "Standard Methods for the Examination of Water and Sewage," Ninth Edition, New York, 1946, p. 126.
46. ——, *op. cit.*, p. 132.
47. ——, *op. cit.*, pp. 132 to 134.
48. ——, *op. cit.*, p. 136.
49. Ruchhoft, C. C., and Placak, O. R., *Sewage Wks J.*, 1942, **14**, 638.
50. Truesdale, G. A., Downing, A. L., and Lowden, G. F., *J. Appl. Chem.*, 1955, **5**, 53.
51. Knudsen, M., "Hydrographic Tables," G. E. C. Gad, Copenhagen, and Williams and Norgate, London, 1901.
52. Hatfield, W. D., and Phillips, C. E., *Waterworks & Sewerage*, 1941, **88**, 285.
53. American Public Health Association, *op. cit.*, p. 140.
54. Ruchhoft, C. C., and Moore, W. A., *Ind. Eng. Chem., Anal. Ed.*, 1940, **12**, 711.
55. Dixon, M., "Manometric Methods," Third Edition, Cambridge University Press, 1951.
56. Gellman, I., and Heukelekian, H., *Sewage Ind. Wastes*, 1951, **23**, 1267.
57. Ludwig, H., Oswald, W. J., and Gotaas, H. B., "Manometric Technique for Measurement of B.O.D.," Institution of Engineering Research, Berkeley, California, 30th June, 1951.
58. American Public Health Association, *op. cit.*, Tenth Edition, p. 329.
59. Wheatland, A. B., and Lloyd, R., *Lab. Practice*, 1955, **4**, 6.
60. Heukelekian, H., and Gellman, I., *Sewage Ind. Wastes*, 1951, **23**, 1546.
61. Lee, E. W., and Oswald, W. J., *Ibid.*, 1954, **26**, 1097.
62. Wooldridge, W. R., and Standfast, A. F. B., *Biochem. J.*, 1936, **30**, 141.

Metallic Contaminants

Preparation of Sample

In most instances, determination of the metallic constituents must be preceded by destruction of the organic matter by oxidation with nitric and sulphuric acids. Certain metals, however, require special treatment, which is described in the appropriate text.

APPARATUS—

This is shown in Fig. 3.

REAGENTS—

Distilled water—To be distilled from glass apparatus.
Nitric acid, sp.gr. 1·42.
Sulphuric acid, sp.gr. 1·84.
Hydrochloric acid, sp.gr. 1·18.
Ammonium oxalate solution, saturated.

PROCEDURE—

Into the 250-ml flask of the apparatus shown in Fig. 3 put a volume of the well mixed sample, the volume being of a suitable size for the particular determination or determinations. Acidify the sample with nitric acid, using about 5 ml in excess. Assemble the apparatus and evaporate the mixture to a volume of 5 to 10 ml. Add 2 to 3 ml of sulphuric acid and continue heating the solution until copious white fumes of sulphur trioxide are evolved. If the solution contains charred organic matter or shows any brown discoloration, carefully add 2 ml of nitric acid and again heat to fuming. If necessary, repeat the treatment with nitric acid until all organic matter is destroyed and the solution becomes colourless. To the cooled solution carefully add 10 ml of saturated ammonium oxalate solution, mix, and again heat to fuming.

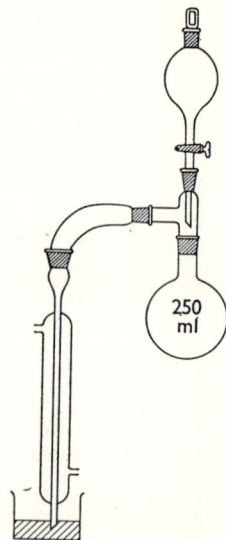

Fig. 3. Apparatus for wet oxidation of the sample

When carrying out the above operations, take care to avoid any sucking back of the distillate. Discard the distillate.

Cool the residue and add 10 ml of distilled water. Allow any insoluble matter to settle and then filter the liquid, receiving the filtrate in a 100-ml calibrated flask and retaining as much of the sediment as possible in the original reaction flask. Add 1 ml of hydrochloric acid to the residue in the flask, heat the solution gently, add 5 ml of hot distilled water and pass the liquid through the filter. Repeat the operation a second time, finally washing the flask and filter with hot distilled water. Cool the combined filtrates and dilute the solution to the mark with distilled water.

Prepare a blank solution in a similar manner, but without the effluent sample.

Aluminium

PRINCIPLE OF METHOD—

In this method,[1] after destruction of the organic matter, the aluminium at pH 4·4 produces a red to pink lake with ammonium aurinetricarboxylate (aluminon) and is determined colorimetrically.

APPLICABILITY—

The method is generally applicable. Substances known not to interfere are: up to 100 μg of ferric iron; up to 10 μg of copper; up to 100 μg of manganese; more than 1000 μg of phosphorus pentoxide (as orthophosphate).

RANGE—

For aluminium contents up to 20 μg.

REAGENTS—

Hydrochloric acid, 5 N—Redistil 250 ml of hydrochloric acid, sp.gr. 1·18, diluted with an equal volume of distilled water, in an all-glass distillation apparatus. Collect the distillate and standardise to 5 N. Store the solution in a stoppered borosilicate-glass bottle.

Starch solution—Mix 1 g of soluble starch with 5 ml of cold distilled water and then add 95 ml of boiling distilled water. Heat to boiling, then cool. Store in a glass bottle in the dark, and prepare freshly every 5 days. Filter before use through a fast filter-paper (Whatman No. 41).

Thioglycollic acid, dilute—Dilute 2 ml of 90 per cent. thioglycollic acid to 100 ml. Prepare freshly every 5 days.

Acetic acid, glacial—Redistil glacial acetic acid in an all-glass apparatus.

Ammonium hydroxide, redistilled—Measure 500 ml of ammonium hydroxide, sp.gr. 0·880, into the flask of an all-glass distillation apparatus. Using a small flame, distil off the ammonia and absorb it in 300 ml of distilled water in a flask surrounded by ice. Guard against the solution sucking back during the distillation. Ascertain the concentration of the purified ammonium hydroxide either by titration or by determining the density.

Ammonium acetate solution—Measure a volume of the redistilled acetic acid equivalent to 210 g of CH_3COOH, dilute it with 100 ml of distilled water and, with stirring, add a volume of the redistilled ammonium hydroxide equivalent to 49·5 g of NH_3. Dilute the solution to 1 litre.

Standard aluminium solution A—Dissolve 1·757 g of aluminium potassium sulphate, $Al_2(SO_4)_3.K_2SO_4.24H_2O$, in distilled water containing 50 ml of 5 N hydrochloric acid and dilute to 1 litre with distilled water.

Standard aluminium solution B—Dilute 5 ml of solution A to 250 ml with distilled water.

$$1 \text{ ml} \equiv 2 \ \mu\text{g of aluminium.}$$

Aluminon, 0·2 per cent. w/v aqueous solution—Dissolve 1 g of the salt (ammonium aurinetricarboxylate) in about 400 ml of distilled water, filter, and then dilute to 500 ml.

Aluminon is known to vary in quality. If the purchased material does not give a satisfactory range of standards, suitable material may be prepared by the following method—

Add 4 g of sodium nitrite slowly in small portions, with vigorous stirring, to 44 ml of concentrated sulphuric acid, sp.gr. 1·84, in a 250-ml beaker, and cool to 10° C. Then add, over a period of 5 to 10 minutes, 12 g of salicylic acid, with stirring. Cool to 3° C in crushed ice and add drop by drop 3·5 ml of an approximately 37 per cent. solution of formaldehyde, with vigorous stirring, keeping the temperature below 5° C. Allow this to remain in the ice-bath for a further hour, stirring every 5 minutes, and then allow the reaction to proceed for 20 hours in the cooling-bath so adjusted that the temperature only rises by 1° to 2° C for the first 7 hours and then gradually attains room temperature (20° C) over the remainder of the period. Next, pour the mixture slowly into 2 litres of cold distilled water, with constant stirring, allow it to stand for 1 hour, and filter it through a Buchner funnel fitted with a close-textured paper. Wash the residue three times with cold distilled water and return it to the beaker. Add 1 litre of distilled water and 50 ml of hydrochloric acid, sp.gr. 1·18, and boil for 2 to 3 minutes. Allow the solid to settle for 10 minutes and wash it three times by decantation with distilled water. Crush and break up the black mass with a flattened glass rod, and twice more repeat the boiling with the same amounts of distilled water and hydrochloric acid, followed by filtration and washing. Finally, dissolve the residue in an excess of ammonium hydroxide and evaporate this solution to dryness on a steam-bath. Grind the dry product to a fine powder and transfer it to a glass-stoppered bottle.

Iron indicator solution—A solution containing 1 μg of ferric iron per ml. Dissolve 0·5 g of ferric chloride, $FeCl_3.6H_2O$, in 100 ml of distilled water; dilute 1 ml of this solution to 1 litre.

PROCEDURE—

Measure into a 50-ml stoppered calibrated flask a suitable volume (not more than 25 ml) of the acid solution, prepared as described under "Preparation of Sample," and containing not more than 20 μg of aluminium. Add 1 ml of iron indicator solution and 2·0 ml of dilute thioglycollic acid; then add redistilled ammonium hydroxide until the colour just changes to violet. Add 2·0 ml of 5 N hydrochloric acid, 3·0 ml of starch solution and 5 ml of ammonium acetate solution, in that order; then dilute to about 45 ml. Add 3·0 ml of aluminon solution, dilute to the 50-ml mark and mix thoroughly. Immerse the flask without the stopper in boiling water for exactly 4 minutes. The flask should be supported in the water bath on a stand approximately $\frac{1}{2}$ inch high to avoid any local overheating.

Carry out a blank procedure on all the reagents.

After heating, remove the flask from the boiling water and allow it to cool gradually to room temperature during 1 hour; then place it in a water bath maintained at a temperature of 20° $\pm$ 0·5° C for 30 minutes. Adjust the volume to 50 ml if necessary and complete the determination colorimetrically by one of the following methods.

Instrumental method—Measure the optical densities of the test and blank solutions in a spectrophotometer or in an absorptiometer, using a 4-cm cell or a 1-cm cell according to the depth of colour, and using a wavelength of 5200 A in a spectrophotometer or a suitable green filter in an absorptiometer. Use distilled water in the comparison cell. Read the number of micrograms of aluminium equivalent to the observed optical densities of the test and blank solutions from a previously prepared calibration graph, and so obtain the net measure of aluminium in the sample.

Establish the calibration graph as follows (NOTE: A new calibration graph should be prepared each time a fresh batch of solid aluminon is used)—

> Measure appropriate amounts of standard aluminium solution B covering the range 0 to 20 μg into a series of 50-ml calibrated flasks and dilute each to about 25 ml. To each add 2·0 ml of 5 N hydrochloric acid, 2·0 ml of dilute thioglycollic acid, 3·0 ml of starch solution and 5 ml of ammonium acetate solution, in that order; then dilute to about 45 ml. Treat each in the same manner as the sample, beginning at "Add 3·0 ml of aluminon solution . . ." in the first paragraph of the Procedure. Measure the optical densities of the solutions, using distilled water in the comparison cell. Construct a graph relating the optical densities to the number of micrograms of aluminium.

Visual colour-comparison method—Prepare a series of standards as described for the Instrumental Method. Compare the colours of the sample and standards either directly in the flasks or after transferring to 50-ml Nessler cylinders.

Express the result as milligrams of aluminium per litre of sample.

REFERENCE

1. Rolfe, A. C., Russell, F. R., and Wilkinson, N. T., *J. Appl. Chem.*, 1951, **1**, 170.

Antimony

PRINCIPLE OF METHOD—

In this method,[1] after destruction of the organic matter, arsenic is removed as the element after reduction with hypophosphite; antimony is then separated by precipitation as the sulphide, brought into solution by a mixture of hydrobromic acid and bromine, reduced by sulphurous acid and determined by titration with potassium bromate.

RANGE—

For antimony contents up to 50 mg.

REAGENTS—

Hydrobromic acid - bromine solution—Dissolve 10 ml of bromine in 100 ml of hydrobromic acid, sp.gr. 1·48. Warm the mixture slightly to dissolve the bromine completely.

Hydrochloric acid, sp.gr. 1·18.

Ammonium hydroxide, sp.gr. 0·880.

Hydrogen peroxide solution, 6 per cent. v/v (20-volume).

Bromine.

Bromine water, saturated.

Hydrogen sulphide gas.

Sulphurous acid—Distilled water saturated with sulphur dioxide.

Potassium bromate solution, 0·05 N—Dissolve 1·392 g of potassium bromate in distilled water, dilute to 1 litre and standardise with arsenious oxide.

Potassium bromate solution, 0·01 N—Make an appropriate dilution of the 0·05 N solution.

Methyl orange indicator solution—A 0·1 per cent. aqueous solution.

PROCEDURE—

Carry out a digestion of a suitable volume of the effluent sample as described under "Preparation of Sample." To the residue in the flask add 20 ml of hydrobromic acid - bromine solution, gently warm the mixture and transfer the solution to a conical flask. Add 10 ml of hydrochloric acid, dilute to 100 ml and boil the solution to remove bromine and until the volume is approximately 75 ml. Cool the solution. If any insoluble matter is present, filter, and wash the filter-paper with distilled water. Collect the filtrate and washings in a 600-ml conical flask and evaporate to a volume of 75 ml. Cool the solution. Add 50 ml of hydrochloric acid; precipitate any arsenic present by means of sodium hypophosphite and filter, as described under "Arsenic: Hypophosphite Method."

Adjust the volume of the filtrate to about 250 ml, add 50 ml of ammonium hydroxide to neutralise most of the acid present, cool, and precipitate the antimony by passing hydrogen sulphide through the solution for about 15 minutes. Immediately filter off the precipitate of antimony sulphide and wash it thoroughly with distilled water saturated with hydrogen sulphide. Place a beaker under the filter funnel, pierce a small hole in the bottom of the filter-paper and wash the precipitate through with distilled water delivered from the jet of a wash-bottle, using only about 25 to 30 ml of water. Dissolve any trace of precipitate remaining on the filter-paper by pouring on to it a hot solution consisting of 20 ml of hydrochloric acid, 4 ml of hydrogen peroxide and 10 ml of saturated bromine water. Wash the filter a few times with distilled water and adjust the final volume to about 100 ml.

To the mixture add 10 drops of bromine and heat to boiling to complete solution of the antimony sulphide. Continue boiling the solution for a few minutes to remove most of the bromine, cool, add 150 ml of sulphurous acid and allow the solution to stand for 1 hour.   Boil the solution to remove sulphur dioxide.   If sulphur dioxide has not been completely removed when the volume of the solution has been reduced to 150 ml, add 100 ml of distilled water and continue boiling.

When the solution is free from sulphur dioxide, add 1 drop of methyl orange indicator solution and titrate the hot solution with potassium bromate solution (0·01 N or 0·05 N, according to the amount of antimony present).

1 ml of 0·01 N potassium bromate solution ≡ 0·000609 g of antimony.

Express the result as milligrams of antimony per litre of sample.

REFERENCE
1.   Wilkinson, N. T., *Analyst*, 1953, **78**, 165.

Arsenic

Two methods are recommended for the determination of arsenic, namely, the Gutzeit method and the hypophosphite method.[1]   It was decided to omit the molybdenum-blue method, since sufficient general experience has not yet been obtained in this country.

GUTZEIT METHOD
PRINCIPLE OF METHOD—

After destruction of the organic matter, arsenic is reduced by means of nascent hydrogen to arsine, which is then passed through mercuric chloride paper and the stain produced is compared with standard arsenic stains.

RANGE—

For arsenic contents up to 10 μg.

APPLICABILITY—

The method is generally applicable.

APPARATUS—

A wide-mouthed bottle capable of holding about 120 ml is fitted with a rubber bung through which passes a glass tube.   The latter, made from ordinary glass tubing, has a total length of 200 mm and an internal diameter of exactly 6·5 mm (external diameter about 8 mm).   It is drawn out at one end to a diameter of about 1 mm and a hole not less than 2 mm in diameter is blown in the side of the tube near the constricted part.   When the bung is inserted in the bottle containing 70 ml of liquid, the constricted end of the tube is above the surface of the liquid and the hole in the side is below the bottom of the bung.   The upper end of the tube is cut off square, and is either slightly flame-polished or ground smooth.

Two rubber bungs (about 25 × 25 mm), each with a hole central and true and exactly 6·5 mm in diameter, are fitted with a rubber band or spring clip for holding them tightly together.   Alternatively, the two bungs may be replaced by any suitable contrivance satisfying the conditions described under "Procedure."

REAGENTS—

NOTE—The reagents must be selected so as to be virtually free from arsenic.   Such reagents can be purchased.

Hydrochloric acid, sp.gr. 1·18.
Stannous chloride solution—Dilute 60 ml of hydrochloric acid with 20 ml of distilled water.   Add 20 g of tin, heat gently until the evolution of gas ceases and

dilute to 100 ml, allowing the undissolved tin to remain in the solution. Add an equal volume of hydrochloric acid. Evaporate the solution to the original volume of 100 ml and filter it through a fine-grained filter-paper.

Stannated hydrochloric acid—Mix 1 ml of stannous chloride solution with 100 ml of hydrochloric acid.

Potassium iodide.

Zinc, granulated (special quality for Gutzeit test).

Standard arsenic solution A—Dissolve 0·132 g of arsenious oxide ($\equiv$100 mg of arsenic) in 50 ml of hydrochloric acid and dilute to 100 ml.

Dilute standard arsenic solution B—Dilute 1 ml of arsenic solution A to 100 ml. Prepare this solution freshly as required.

$$1 \text{ ml} \equiv 10 \text{ }\mu\text{g of arsenic.}$$

Lead acetate solution, 10 per cent. w/v.

Mercuric chloride paper—Smooth white filter-paper, not less than 25 mm in width, soaked in a saturated solution of mercuric chloride in distilled water, pressed to remove superfluous solution, and dried at about 60° C in the dark. The grade of the filter-paper shall be such that the weight in g per sq. metre shall be between 65 and 120; the thickness in millimetres of 400 papers shall be approximately equal, numerically, to the weight in g per sq. metre.

NOTE—Store the prepared paper in a stoppered bottle. Papers that are available commercially have been found to produce more uniform results than those prepared in the laboratory.

PROCEDURE—

Pack the glass tube of the apparatus lightly with cotton-wool that has been previously moistened with a solution of lead acetate and dried, so that the upper surface of the cotton-wool is not less than 25 mm below the top of the tube. Insert the upper end of the tube into the narrow end of one of the pair of rubber bungs, either to a depth of about 10 mm when the tube has a flame-polished end, or so that the ground end of the tube is flush with the larger end of the bung. Place a piece of mercuric chloride paper flat on the top of the bung, place the other bung over it and secure the two by means of a rubber band or spring clip in such a manner that the bores of the two bungs meet to form a true bore, 6·5 mm in diameter, interrupted by the diaphragm of mercuric chloride paper. This method of attaching the mercuric chloride paper may be replaced by any other method, provided that—

(*a*) the whole of the evolved gases pass through the paper,

(*b*) the portion of the paper in contact with the gas is a circle 6·5 mm in diameter, and

(*c*) the paper is protected from sunlight during the test.

Transfer an aliquot (preferably containing about 5 μg of arsenic) of the acid solution, prepared as described under "Preparation of Sample," to the wide-mouthed bottle and dilute it to 50 ml. Add 10 ml of stannated hydrochloric acid, 1 g of potassium iodide and, finally, 10 g of granulated zinc. Immediately place the prepared glass tube in position. Allow the reaction to proceed for 40 minutes at a temperature not exceeding 40° C; adjust the temperature to obtain a regular, but not too violent, evolution of gas.

Compare the yellow stain produced on the mercuric chloride paper with a series of standard stains produced as described below.

The standard stains should be prepared at the same time as the test stain.

Carry out the procedure on the same volume of the blank solution referred to under "Preparation of Sample." This stain should be negligible.

Express the result as milligrams of arsenic per litre of sample.

PREPARATION OF STANDARD STAINS—

Six sets of apparatus are required for the preparation of the standard stains. Charge each tube with cotton-wool, previously moistened with a solution of lead acetate and dried, and fix a piece of mercuric chloride paper as described under "Procedure." Into the wide-mouthed bottles measure quantities of dilute standard arsenic solution B varying from 0 to 1 ml in steps of 0·2 ml. Dilute the contents of each bottle to 50 ml, add 10 ml of stannated hydrochloric acid, 1 g of potassium iodide and 10 g of granulated zinc, and immediately place the prepared glass tube in position. Allow the reaction to proceed as described under "Procedure."

HYPOPHOSPHITE METHOD

PRINCIPLE OF METHOD—

The arsenic present is reduced to elementary arsenic. This is separated by filtration and determined iodimetrically.

RANGE—

For arsenic contents of 0·4 to 100 mg.

NOTE—For arsenic contents less than 0·4 mg and greater than 10 μg, the sample should be suitably diluted and the Gutzeit method applied.

APPLICABILITY—

The method is of wide applicability, although mercury, selenium and tellurium interfere.

REAGENTS—

Sodium arsenite solution, 0·1 N—Weigh 4·9455 g of arsenious oxide, previously dried at 105° C. Dissolve this in a solution of sodium hydroxide (2·5 g of sodium hydroxide pellets dissolved in about 50 ml of distilled water), with gentle warming. Cool the solution, add 66 ml of N hydrochloric acid and then 10 g of sodium bicarbonate. Transfer the solution to a 1-litre calibrated flask and dilute to the mark with distilled water.

Sodium arsenite solution, 0·01 N—Dilute the 0·1 N sodium arsenite solution, 1 in 10 with distilled water.

Iodine solution, 0·1 N.

Iodine solution, 0·01 N.

Hydrochloric acid, sp.gr. 1·18.

Sodium hypophosphite.

Ammonium chloride solution, 5 per cent. w/v.

Potassium iodide.

Sodium bicarbonate.

Filtering medium—Digest about twenty 11-cm filter-papers (Whatman No. 40) in 400 ml of distilled water containing 4 ml of hydrochloric acid and 20 ml of saturated bromine water on a water bath for about 4 hours. Store the pulped material in a glass-stoppered bottle. When preparing the filter-pad, wash it thoroughly with distilled water before using the filter.

PROCEDURE—

Transfer a suitable aliquot of the acid solution, prepared as described under "Preparation of Sample," to a conical flask and dilute it to 75 ml with distilled water. Add 75 ml of hydrochloric acid and 4 g of sodium hypophosphite. Heat the solution for 5 minutes, but do not allow the temperature to rise above 50° C. Add a further 10 g of sodium hypophosphite, and close the mouth of the flask with a cork carrying a length of glass tubing, approximately 80 cm long and 0·5 cm internal diameter, to act as a reflux condenser. Bring the solution to boiling-point and boil gently for 15 minutes. Cool, and collect the precipitated arsenic on a pad of the previously prepared filter-pulp. If large amounts of arsenic are present, it is advisable to mix a little of the washed filter-pulp with the precipitate in the conical flask before filtering, in order to keep the precipitate in a finely divided condition, so that it will readily dissolve in the iodine solution used for the titration. Wash the precipitate on the filter-pad with an acid solution of sodium hypophosphite, prepared by adding 2 g of sodium hypophosphite to 100 ml of a solution of diluted hydrochloric acid (1 + 3). Finally wash the precipitate with ammonium chloride solution to remove sodium hypophosphite.

Transfer the precipitate and paper pulp to a 16-oz wide-mouthed glass-stoppered bottle containing about 50 ml of distilled water. Disintegrate the precipitate and paper pulp, and add 2 g of potassium iodide and 2 g of sodium bicarbonate. Then add 0·1 N iodine solution (or 0·01 N, the particular strength of iodine solution to be used depending upon the amount of precipitate) sufficient to react with the arsenic and to give about 10 ml in excess. Shake the contents of the bottle thoroughly to dissolve the arsenic. Remove the stopper, rinsing it with distilled water, and immediately titrate the excess of iodine with either 0·1 N or 0·01 N sodium arsenite solution, according to the concentration of the iodine solution used. The end-point, *i.e.*, the change from the yellow of the iodine solution to the white of the oxycellulose pulp, is quite sharp.

$$\frac{\text{Volume (ml) of } 0 \cdot 1 \, N \text{ iodine solution} \times 0 \cdot 00149 \times 10^6}{\text{Volume (ml) of original sample}} = \text{Arsenic content (mg per litre)}.$$

REFERENCE

1. Haslam, J., and Wilkinson, N. T., *Analyst*, 1953, **78**, 390.

Barium Soluble in Dilute Hydrochloric Acid

PRINCIPLE OF METHOD—

After the masking of any lead or strontium present, barium is precipitated under controlled conditions as the sulphate, which is measured turbidimetrically.

RANGE—

For barium contents up to 1·5 mg.

NOTE—It is possible to measure barium contents greater than 1·5 mg by this method, but it has been found that different batches of sodium sulphate (although of the same mesh size) give rise to irregularities of the calibration graph in the higher range. If it is desired, therefore, to determine barium above the recommended range, a fresh calibration graph should be made for each batch of sodium sulphate.

APPLICABILITY—

The method is generally applicable. The possible interference of lead and strontium is avoided by the addition of ethylenediaminetetra-acetic acid.

REAGENTS—

Hydrochloric acid, N.
Sodium hydroxide solution, N.
Acid sodium chloride solution—Dissolve 58·5 g of sodium chloride in distilled water, add 200 ml of N hydrochloric acid and dilute to 1 litre with distilled water.
EDTA solution—Dissolve 37·23 g of disodium ethylenediaminetetra-acetate dihydrate (EDTA) in distilled water and dilute to 1 litre.
Glycerol solution—A 40 per cent. v/v solution in distilled water.

E

Sodium sulphate, anhydrous—Graded, passing a B.S. 18-mesh sieve and retained on a B.S. 30-mesh sieve.

Standard barium solution—Dissolve 0·1778 g of barium chloride, $BaCl_2.2H_2O$, in distilled water and dilute to 1 litre.

$$1 \text{ ml} \equiv 100 \text{ mg of barium.}$$

Methyl orange indicator solution—A 0·1 per cent. w/v aqueous solution.

PROCEDURE—

(The test and calibration must be carried out at the same temperature, *i.e.*, $20° \pm 2° C.$)

First determine the amount of acid or alkali (using methyl orange as indicator) required to neutralise a suitable aliquot of the well shaken effluent.

Then measure two portions of the well shaken effluent, containing not more than 1·5 mg of barium, and neutralise each accordingly. To each solution add 1 ml of N hydrochloric acid and boil. If necessary, continue boiling until the volume is reduced to about 35 ml. Filter each solution into a separate 100-ml calibrated flask, washing the filter-paper with two 5-ml portions of distilled water; add 1 ml of N sodium hydroxide solution and 5 ml of EDTA solution and then 15 ml of acid sodium chloride solution and 25 ml of glycerol solution, mixing after the addition of each reagent. Dilute each solution to the mark with distilled water and mix well.

Pour one of the solutions into a 150-ml stoppered conical flask, add 0·3 g of anhydrous sodium sulphate, replace the stopper and gently swirl the mixture for 2 minutes. Allow to stand for 5 minutes and then compare the turbidities by measuring the optical densities of both solutions (the untreated solution being used as a blank) absorptiometrically, with neutral filters and using distilled water in the comparison cell. Read the number of milligrams of barium equivalent to the observed optical densities of the test and blank solutions from a previously prepared calibration graph, and so obtain the net measure of barium in the sample.

Express the result as milligrams of barium per litre of sample.

Establish the calibration graph as follows—

Measure appropriate amounts of standard barium solution, covering the range 0 to 1·5 mg, into a series of 100-ml calibrated flasks. Dilute each to 50 ml with distilled water, add 5 ml of EDTA solution and proceed as described for the test solution. Measure the optical densities and, after correcting the readings for a blank with no added barium, construct a graph relating the optical densities to the number of milligrams of barium.

Cadmium

PRINCIPLE OF METHOD—

In this method,[1] after destruction of the organic matter, cadmium is determined colorimetrically as its red complex with dithizone.

RANGE—

For cadmium contents of (*a*) up to 50 μg (instrumental method)
or (*b*) up to 25 μg (visual colour-comparison method).

APPLICABILITY—

The method is generally applicable, but copper and nickel interfere unless complexed with cyanide.

REAGENTS—

Sodium hydroxide solution, 20 per cent. w/v.

Potassium sodium tartrate solution—Dissolve 25 g of potassium sodium tartrate, $C_4H_4O_6KNa.4H_2O$, in 100 ml of distilled water.

Sodium hydroxide - potassium cyanide solution A—Dissolve 40 g of sodium hydroxide and 1·0 g of potassium cyanide in 100 ml of distilled water.

Sodium hydroxide - potassium cyanide solution B—Dissolve 40 g of sodium hydroxide and 0·05 g of potassium cyanide in 100 ml of distilled water.

Hydroxylamine hydrochloride solution—Dissolve 20 g of hydroxylamine hydrochloride in 100 ml of distilled water. Transfer the solution to a separating funnel and extract with a 0·01 per cent. w/v solution of dithizone in carbon tetrachloride, using 5-ml portions until the last extract remains green; then wash the solution free from excess of dithizone by repeated extraction with 10-ml portions of carbon tetrachloride. Transfer the solution to a beaker, warm to remove excess of carbon tetrachloride, cool and filter into a 100-ml flask.

Carbon tetrachloride, redistilled.

Dithizone stock solution—Dissolve 0·1 g of diphenylthiocarbazone (dithizone) in 100 ml of redistilled carbon tetrachloride.

Dithizone extraction solution—Extract 15 ml of the dithizone stock solution with two 50-ml portions of dilute ammonium hydroxide (50 ml of distilled water containing 2 ml of 10 M ammonium hydroxide) and reject the carbon tetrachloride layer. Filter the combined ammoniacal extracts if necessary. Acidify the extract with dilute hydrochloric acid (about 1 per cent.) and extract the precipitated dithizone with 100 ml of carbon tetrachloride. Wash the extract with two 10-ml portions of distilled water and filter it through a dry filter-paper.

Tartaric acid solution—Dissolve 2 g of tartaric acid in 100 ml of distilled water.

Standard cadmium solution—Dissolve 0·100 g of cadmium metal in 50 ml of 10 per cent. nitric acid. Boil the solution to expel oxides of nitrogen and dilute to 1 litre with distilled water. Dilute 10 ml of this solution to 100 ml. Prepare this dilute solution freshly as required.

$$1 \text{ ml} \equiv 10 \ \mu g \text{ of cadmium.}$$

PROCEDURE—

Measure into a separating funnel a suitable aliquot of the acid solution prepared as described under "Preparation of Sample," and containing not more than 50 μg of cadmium. Neutralise with sodium hydroxide solution and adjust the volume to 25 ml.

Add 1 ml of potassium sodium tartrate solution, 5 ml of sodium hydroxide - potassium cyanide solution A and 1 ml of hydroxylamine hydrochloride solution, mixing after each addition. Add 10 ml of dithizone extraction solution, shake the mixture for 1 minute, allow the layers to separate and run the lower layer into a second separating funnel containing 25 ml of tartaric acid solution.

Repeat the extraction with further 10-ml portions of dithizone extraction solution, adding the lower layer to the tartaric acid solution contained in the second separating funnel, until no pink colour appears in the last extract.

Shake the combined extracts with the tartaric acid solution in the second separating funnel for 2 minutes. Allow to separate and discard the lower layer. Add 5 ml of carbon tetrachloride, shake for 1 minute, allow to separate and discard the lower layer.

Add 0·25 ml of hydroxylamine hydrochloride solution, 10 ml of dithizone extraction solution followed by 5 ml of sodium hydroxide - potassium cyanide solution B, and shake the mixture for 1 minute. Allow the layers to separate and filter the carbon tetrachloride layer through a toughened filter-paper (Whatman No. 541 is suitable) into a 50-ml calibrated flask.   Continue to extract the aqueous layer remaining in the funnel with further 10-ml portions of dithizone extraction solution until no pink colour appears in the final extract, filtering each successive extract through the filter-paper into the calibrated flask.   Dilute the bulked extract to the mark with carbon tetrachloride and mix.

Carry out a blank procedure on all the reagents used.

Measure the optical densities of the test and blank solutions in a spectrophotometer or in an absorptiometer, using a 4-cm or a 1-cm cell according to the depth of colour, and using a wavelength of 5250 A in a spectrophotometer or a suitable green filter in an absorptiometer.   Use carbon tetrachloride in the comparison cell.   Read the number of micrograms of cadmium equivalent to the observed optical densities of the test and blank solutions from a previously prepared calibration graph, and so obtain the net measure of cadmium in the sample.

Express the result as milligrams of cadmium per litre of sample.

Establish the calibration graph as follows—

Measure appropriate amounts of standard cadmium solution covering the range 0 to 50 μg into a series of separating funnels.   Neutralise as necessary with 20 per cent. sodium hydroxide solution and adjust the volume to 25 ml.   Proceed as described above, beginning at "Add 1 ml of potassium sodium tartrate solution . . .," in the second paragraph.   Measure the optical densities and construct a graph relating the optical densities to the number of micrograms of cadmium.

If an instrument is not available, colours may be matched visually in 50-ml Nessler cylinders, a series of standards covering the range 0 to 25 μg of cadmium being used.

REFERENCE

1.   Saltzmann, B. E., *Anal. Chem.*, 1953, **25**, 493.

Chromium

TOTAL CHROMIUM

PRINCIPLE OF METHOD—

After destruction of the organic matter, all the chromium present is oxidised to chromate, which is determined colorimetrically as the violet-coloured complex with diphenylcarbazide.

RANGE—

For chromium contents up to 20 μg.

REAGENTS—

Distilled water—This should be specially prepared by distilling tap water to which sulphuric acid and a few crystals of potassium permanganate have been added. Suitable precautions must be taken to exclude atmospheric dust during distillation and storage.

This specially prepared water must be used for the reagents and throughout the procedure.

Sulphuric acid, sp.gr. 1·84.
Nitric acid, sp.gr. 1·42.
Ammonium oxalate solution, saturated.
Sodium sulphite—$Na_2SO_3.7H_2O$.

Phosphoric acid, 60 *per cent.*
Potassium permanganate solution, 1 *per cent. w/v.*
Sodium hydroxide solution, 15 *per cent. w/v.*
Hydrogen peroxide, 3 *per cent. v/v* (10-*volume*).
*Diphenylcarbazide solution—Dissolve 0·25 g of diphenylcarbazide in 25 ml of ethanol and dilute to 100 ml with distilled water.
*Sulphuric acid, dilute, 5 *per cent. v/v.*
*Standard chromium solution—Dissolve 0·3740 g of potassium chromate in distilled water and dilute to 1 litre. Dilute 10 ml of this solution to 500 ml. Prepare this dilute solution freshly as required.

$$1 \text{ ml} \equiv 2 \text{ } \mu g \text{ of chromium.}$$

PROCEDURE—

Place 100 ml (or a suitable volume) of the effluent sample in a 250-ml Kjeldahl flask and dissolve in it 0·1 g of sodium sulphite. Add 2 ml of concentrated sulphuric acid and evaporate until white fumes of sulphur trioxide are evolved. If necessary, add concentrated nitric acid drop by drop to oxidise any residual organic matter. Add 10 ml of saturated ammonium oxalate solution and evaporate once more to fumes. When cool, dilute the solution with 10 ml of distilled water and transfer the contents of the Kjeldahl flask to a 25-ml calibrated flask, and dilute to the mark.

Mix well and place 5 ml, or a larger aliquot if necessary, in a small beaker, add 5 drops of phosphoric acid and evaporate to fumes. Cool the solution, add 1 ml of potassium permanganate solution, cover the beaker with a watch-glass and heat on a water bath for 20 minutes.

Neutralise the solution to litmus paper with sodium hydroxide solution and add 1 ml in excess. Add 2 ml of the hydrogen peroxide and allow the solution to simmer gently on a hot-plate for 10 minutes. Cool the solution, dilute it to 20 ml in a calibrated flask and filter. Measure accurately a volume of the filtrate (5 to 10 ml) into a 25-ml calibrated flask, add 5 ml of dilute sulphuric acid and dilute the solution to about 20 ml. Add 2·5 ml of diphenylcarbazide solution and dilute the solution to the mark. Allow the solution to stand for 5 minutes before the colour measurement.

Carry out a blank procedure on all the reagents used.

Measure the optical density in a spectrophotometer or in an absorptiometer, using a wavelength of 5400 A in a spectrophotometer, or a suitable green filter in an absorptiometer. Read the number of micrograms of chromium equivalent to the observed optical densities of the test and blank solutions from a previously prepared calibration graph, and so obtain the net measure of chromium in the sample.

As the violet colour fades on standing, the colour measurement should be carried out after 5 minutes.

Express the result as milligrams of chromium per litre of sample.

Establish the calibration graph as follows—

Measure appropriate amounts of standard chromium solution covering the range 0 to 20 μg of chromium into a series of 25-ml calibrated flasks. Add to each 5 ml of dilute sulphuric acid and dilute the solution to about 20 ml. Add 2·5 ml of diphenylcarbazide solution and dilute each solution to the mark. Allow the solutions to stand for 5 minutes and then measure the optical densities and construct a graph relating the optical densities to the number of micrograms of chromium.

If an instrument is not available, colours may be matched visually against a series of standards.

CHROMIUM PRESENT IN THE EFFLUENT AS CHROMATE

It may sometimes be useful to determine the chromium present as chromate, and the method below is recommended, with the following reservations—

(*a*)   it is not applicable when the effluent itself is highly coloured, and
(*b*)   chromate tends to disappear in the effluent owing to reduction by organic impurities.

PRINCIPLE OF METHOD—

The chromate in the effluent sample is directly determined colorimetrically as the violet-coloured complex with diphenylcarbazide.

RANGE—

For chromium contents up to 20 μg.

REAGENTS—

Those marked with an asterisk (*) in the method for "Total Chromium."

PROCEDURE—

Place 25 ml of the effluent sample in a 50-ml cylinder and add 5 ml of diphenyl-carbazide solution; then add 10 ml of dilute sulphuric acid, with mixing, and dilute the solution to 50 ml. Allow it to stand for 5 minutes and measure the optical density as described in the method for "Total Chromium."

If the solution under test is turbid, clear it before applying the test either by centrifuging it or by filtering it in an alkaline condition, using a filter aid.

Copper

PRINCIPLE OF METHOD—

After destruction of the organic matter, the copper is extracted from alkaline citrate solution as its diethyldithiocarbamate and then determined colorimetrically.

RANGE—

For copper contents up to 50 μg.

APPLICABILITY—

The method is of wide applicability, although bismuth interferes.

REAGENTS—

NOTE—Water distilled from glass apparatus must be used throughout.

Sodium diethyldithiocarbamate solution—Dissolve 1 g of sodium diethyldi-thiocarbamate in 100 ml of water and filter the solution.

EDTA - citrate solution—Dissolve 20 g of ammonium citrate and 5 g of disodium ethylenediaminetetra-acetate (EDTA) in water and dilute to 100 ml with water.

Standard copper solution—Dissolve 0·200 g of pure copper wire in 15 ml of diluted nitric acid (1 +4), boil to expel fumes, cool and dilute to 200 ml with water. Dilute 10 ml of this solution to 1 litre as required.

$$1 \text{ ml} \equiv 10 \text{ μg of copper.}$$

Ammonium hydroxide, sp.gr. 0·880.
Cresol red indicator solution, 0·04 per cent. in ethanol (I.M.S.).
Carbon tetrachloride.

PROCEDURE—

Transfer 25 to 50 ml of the acid solution, prepared as described under "Preparation of Sample" and containing not more than 50 μg of copper, to a separating funnel. Add 10 ml of EDTA - citrate solution and 2 drops of cresol red indicator solution. Add ammonium hydroxide until the solution is purple-red, cool and add 1 ml of sodium diethyldithiocarbamate solution. Add 10 ml of carbon tetrachloride and shake the funnel for 2 minutes. Allow the layers to separate; then remove the lower layer and filter it through a dry filter-paper into a 25-ml calibrated flask. Extract the aqueous layer with further 5-ml portions of carbon tetrachloride until no further colour is extracted. Filter the extracts as before through the same filter-paper and dilute to the mark with carbon tetrachloride. Measure the optical density in a spectrophotometer or an absorptiometer, using a wavelength of 4320 A in a spectrophotometer, or a suitable blue filter if an absorptiometer is used. Read the number of micrograms of copper equivalent to the observed optical densities of the test and blank solutions from a previously prepared calibration graph, and so obtain the net measure of copper in the sample.

Express the result as milligrams of copper per litre of sample.

Establish the calibration graph as follows—

To 50 ml of glass-distilled water containing 1 ml of sulphuric acid, add appropriate amounts of standard copper solution to cover the range 5 to 50 µg, and proceed as described above. Construct a graph relating optical densities to micrograms of copper.

INTERFERENCE OF BISMUTH—

Bismuth is also extracted by the carbamate reagent under the conditions described above. If bismuth is present, the determination should be repeated, with potassium cyanide solution added before the sodium diethyldithiocarbamate solution, and the second reading should be subtracted from the first to give the optical density due to the copper.

Iron

PRINCIPLE OF METHOD—

After destruction of the organic matter, the iron is determined colorimetrically as the purple thioglycollate.

RANGE—

For iron contents of (a) up to 1000 µg (instrumental method)
or (b) up to 100 µg (visual colour-comparison method).

APPLICABILITY—

The method is generally applicable. Cobalt gives a yellow-red colour and must be absent. Copper and zinc tend to reduce the colour due to iron, but addition of more reagent overcomes this interference. Nickel interferes if present in similar amounts to iron.

REAGENTS—

Thioglycollic acid, 10 *per cent.* v/v—Store in an amber-coloured bottle; discard after 1 month.

NOTE—The concentrated acid may attack the skin.

Standard iron solution A—Dissolve 0·702 g of ferrous ammonium sulphate in about 300 ml of distilled water containing 2 ml of concentrated sulphuric acid. Dilute this solution to 1 litre in a calibrated flask.

1 ml ≡ 100 µg of iron.

Standard iron solution B—Dilute 10·0 ml of standard iron solution A to 100 ml in a calibrated flask. Prepare this solution freshly as required.

$$1 \text{ ml} \equiv 10 \ \mu g \text{ of iron.}$$

Hydrochloric acid, sp.gr. 1·18.
Citric acid solution, 20 *per cent. w/v.*
Ammonium hydroxide, sp.gr. 0·880.

PROCEDURE—

Measure an aliquot (not exceeding 20 ml) of the acid solution, prepared as described under "Preparation of Sample," into a 50-ml calibrated flask. Dilute the solution to about 40 ml with distilled water. Add 2 ml of 20 per cent. citric acid solution, 1 ml of 10 per cent. thioglycollic acid and 4 ml of ammonium hydroxide, mixing the solution after each addition. Dilute this solution to the mark and mix well.

Carry out the procedure on the same volume of the blank solution referred to under "Preparation of Sample."

Determine the amount of iron present in the solution by measurement of the colour, either instrumentally, or by visual comparison against a series of standard colours.

Express the result as milligrams of iron per litre of sample.

Instrumental method—Measure the optical densities of the test and blank solutions in a spectrophotometer or in an absorptiometer, using a 4-cm or a 1-cm cell, according to the depth of colour, and using a wavelength of 4900 A in a spectrophotometer or a suitable blue or blue-green filter in an absorptiometer. Use water in the comparison cell. Read the number of micrograms of iron equivalent to the observed optical densities of the test and blank solutions from a previously prepared calibration graph, and so obtain the net measure of iron in the sample.

Establish the calibration graph as follows—

Measure the appropriate amounts of standard iron solution A or B into a series of 50-ml calibrated flasks. For the 4-cm cell the standards should cover the range 0 to 200 μg of iron; for the 1-cm cell they should cover the range 0 to 1000 μg of iron. Dilute the contents of each flask to 40 ml with distilled water. Add 1 ml of hydrochloric acid, 2 ml of citric acid solution, 1 ml of thioglycollic acid solution and 2·5 ml of ammonium hydroxide, mixing the solution well after each addition. Dilute each solution to the mark and mix. Measure the optical densities and construct a graph relating the optical densities to the number of micrograms of iron.

Visual colour-comparison method—Transfer the test solution to a 50-ml Nessler cylinder and compare the colour against a series of standards prepared as follows—

Into a series of 50-ml Nessler cylinders measure volumes between 0 and 10 ml of standard iron solution B and dilute each to about 40 ml. Add to each solution 1 ml of hydrochloric acid, 2 ml of citric acid solution, 1 ml of thioglycollic acid solution and 2·5 ml of ammonium hydroxide, mixing the solutions well after each addition. Dilute each solution to the mark.

Lead

PRINCIPLE OF METHOD—

After destruction of the organic matter, lead is extracted from ammoniacal cyanide solution as the pink lead dithizonate, interfering metals being first removed by extraction in acid solution. The lead is then determined colorimetrically.

RANGE—

For lead contents of (*a*) up to 100 μg (instrumental method)
or (*b*) up to 15 μg (visual colour-comparison method).

APPLICABILITY—

The method is generally applicable. Relatively large amounts of calcium phosphate interfere.

APPARATUS—

NOTE—Lead-free borosilicate-glass apparatus must be used throughout.

Titration flask—This is shown in Fig. 4.

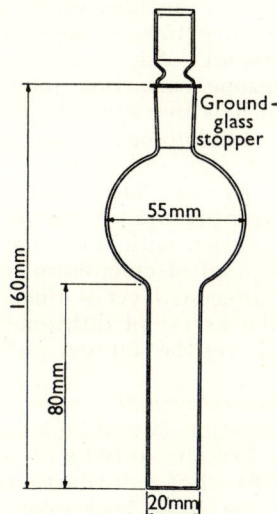

Fig. 4. Titration flask

REAGENTS—

NOTE—Lead-free distilled water must be used throughout.

Chloroform, redistilled—Redistil chloroform in an all-glass distillation apparatus.

Ammonium hydroxide, approximately 10 M—Dilute 1 volume of ammonium hydroxide, sp.gr. 0·880, with 1 volume of distilled water.

Ammonium hydroxide, diluted—Dilute 1 volume of ammonium hydroxide, sp. gr. 0·880, with 2 volumes of distilled water.

Hydrochloric acid, sp.gr. 1·18, *redistilled.*

Hydrochloric acid, diluted (1 + 1).

Nitric acid, redistilled—Redistil nitric acid, sp.gr. 1·42, in an all-glass distillation apparatus.

Nitric acid, diluted (1 + 3).

Nitric acid, dilute (*about* 1 *per cent.*).

Dithizone stock solution—Dissolve 0·05 g of diphenylthiocarbazone (dithizone) in 100 ml of redistilled chloroform.

Dithizone extraction solution A—Extract 15 ml of the dithizone stock solution with two 50-ml portions of dilute ammonium hydroxide (50 ml of distilled water containing 2 ml of 10 *M* ammonium hydroxide) and then reject the chloroform layer. Filter the combined ammoniacal extracts if necessary. Acidify the extract with diluted hydrochloric acid, and extract the precipitated dithizone with 100 ml of chloroform. Wash the extract with two 10-ml portions of distilled water, and filter it through a dry filter-paper. Prepare this solution freshly each day.

Dithizone extraction solution B—Dilute 20 ml of dithizone extraction solution A to 100 ml with chloroform.

Hydroxylamine hydrochloride solution—Dissolve 25 g of hydroxylamine hydrochloride in about 60 ml of distilled water, add 0·2 ml of thymol blue indicator solution and make alkaline with 10 M ammonium hydroxide to the full blue colour of the indicator. Cool and extract the solution with dithizone extraction solution A, using 5-ml portions, until the last extract remains green; then wash the aqueous solution free from the excess of dithizone by repeated extraction with 10-ml portions of chloroform. Warm the solution until the excess of chloroform has been removed, cool, filter and dilute to 250 ml with distilled water.

Sodium citrate solution—Dissolve 150 g of sodium citrate, $Na_3C_6H_5O_7.2H_2O$, in distilled water and dilute to 500 ml. Add 3 drops of ammonium hydroxide and extract the solution with dithizone extraction solution A in slight excess; then wash the aqueous solution until it is free from the excess of dithizone by repeated extraction with 10-ml portions of chloroform. Warm the solution until the excess of chloroform has been removed, cool and filter.

Potassium cyanide solution—Dissolve 50 g of potassium cyanide in the minimum amount of distilled water and transfer the solution to a separating funnel. Dilute it to 100 ml and extract the solution with dithizone extraction solution A, using 5-ml portions to each of which 5 ml of chloroform has been added, until the last extract remains green and the aqueous layer is tinged yellow. Wash the aqueous solution until it is free from the excess of dithizone by repeated extraction with 10-ml portions of chloroform. Filter the solution and dilute to 500 ml with distilled water.

Ammonium hydroxide - potassium cyanide solution—Mix 45 ml of 10 M ammonium hydroxide and 40 ml of the potassium cyanide solution and dilute to 200 ml.

Standard lead solution A—Dissolve 0·160 g of lead nitrate, dried at 100° C, in 50 ml of distilled water and 10 ml of redistilled nitric acid, and dilute to 100 ml in a calibrated flask. This is the stock lead solution. Measure 10·0 ml of this solution into a 1-litre calibrated flask, add 9 ml of redistilled nitric acid, dilute to the mark with distilled water and mix well. Prepare this solution freshly as required.

$$1 \text{ ml} \equiv 10 \ \mu g \text{ of lead.}$$

Standard lead solution B—Dilute 10·0 ml of standard lead solution A to 50 ml in a calibrated flask. Prepare this solution freshly as required.

$$1 \text{ ml} \equiv 2 \ \mu g \text{ of lead.}$$

Methyl orange indicator solution—A 0·04 per cent. aqueous solution.
Thymol blue indicator solution—A 0·025 per cent. aqueous solution.
m-*Cresol purple indicator solution*—A 0·05 per cent. aqueous solution.

PROCEDURE—

Measure 100 ml of the effluent sample (see Note) into a 400-ml beaker, add 2 drops of methyl orange indicator solution, just acidify with redistilled nitric acid and then add 10 ml of the acid in excess. Evaporate the solution to a volume of 10 to 15 ml and transfer it to a small glass dish, using the minimum amount of distilled water for rinsing. Evaporate the solution to dryness on a steam-bath. Wash down the sides of the dish with 5 ml of redistilled nitric acid, and again evaporate the solution to complete dryness on the steam-bath. Transfer the dish to an electrically heated muffle furnace controlled at 490° to 500° C and ignite for 15 minutes. Allow the dish and contents to cool, add 3 ml of redistilled nitric acid and 15 ml of distilled water, and heat for 5 minutes on the steam-bath. Filter the contents through a small Whatman No. 540 filter-paper and wash the residue with small amounts of hot diluted nitric acid (1 + 3); cool the filtrate.

Add 2 ml of hydroxylamine hydrochloride solution, 2 ml of sodium citrate solution and 2 drops of thymol blue indicator solution. Add 10 M ammonium hydroxide until the indicator colour changes to full blue; cool again. The solution should be quite clear at this point; if not, re-acidify it and increase the amount of sodium citrate solution. Add 0·5 ml of 10 M ammonium hydroxide in excess and 3 to 5 ml of potassium cyanide solution. Transfer the solution to a 100-ml pear-shaped separating funnel and adjust the volume to about 35 ml.

Extract the lead with dithizone extraction solution A, using 3 ml for each extraction. Shake the funnel vigorously for 30 seconds after each addition until all the lead is extracted; this is indicated by two consecutive extracts remaining green. Collect the chloroform extracts in a second separating funnel and reject the aqueous layer. Wash the combined chloroform extracts with 50 ml of distilled water and run the chloroform layer into the first funnel; wash the distilled water with two 5-ml portions of chloroform and add these washings to the main chloroform extract of the lead dithizonate.

Shake the chloroform extract with 25 ml of dilute nitric acid (1 per cent.) for 1 minute, allow the layers to separate and reject all but 0·5 ml of the chloroform layer; this 0·5 ml is left for the detection of the presence or absence of bismuth, which would interfere unless removed at this stage. Adjust the nitric acid extract to pH 2 by adding 2 or 3 drops of *m*-cresol purple indicator solution followed by the addition, drop by drop, of diluted ammonium hydroxide (1 + 2) until the colour of the indicator changes to orange-pink. Shake the contents of the separating funnel vigorously for 30 seconds; if bismuth is present the 0·5 ml of dithizone in chloroform will change colour.

If bismuth is present, remove it from the acid solution by repeated extractions with 5-ml portions of dithizone extraction solution A. When all the bismuth has been extracted, wash the solution free from dithizone with chloroform.

If bismuth is absent, reject the 0·5 ml of dithizone in chloroform solution and wash the acid solution free from dithizone with chloroform.

Carry out a blank procedure on all the reagents used.

Proceed to determine the lead colorimetrically, either by the instrumental method or by the visual colour-comparison method described below.

Express the result as milligrams of lead per litre of sample.

Instrumental method—Treat the blank and test solutions similarly. To the dithizone-free solution add 3 ml of the ammonium hydroxide - potassium cyanide solution and re-extract the lead by shaking with 3-ml portions of dithizone extraction solution A. Collect the chloroform extracts.

To the combined chloroform extracts add 10 ml of a diluted ammonium hydroxide - potassium cyanide solution (4 ml of 10 M ammonium hydroxide and 1 ml of potassium cyanide solution in 100 ml of distilled water), shake the mixture for 10 seconds, allow the layers to separate and return the chloroform layer to the first separating funnel, rejecting the aqueous layer. Again wash the chloroform solution with 10 ml of the diluted ammonium hydroxide - potassium cyanide solution, shake for 10 seconds and allow the layers to separate: repeat this washing of the chloroform layer once more. Filter the chloroform layer through a dry Whatman No. 41 filter-paper into a dry 25-ml calibrated flask, and wash out the separating funnel with successive small amounts of chloroform, filtering each washing into the flask; dilute the solution to the mark with chloroform and mix well.

Measure the optical densities of the test and blank solutions in a spectrophotometer or in an absorptiometer, using a 4-cm or a 1-cm cell according to the depth of colour, and using a wavelength of 5500 A in a spectrophotometer or a suitable yellow-green filter in an absorptiometer.   Use chloroform in the comparison cell. Read the number of micrograms of lead equivalent to the observed optical densities of the test and blank solutions from a previously prepared calibration graph, and so obtain the net measure of lead in the sample.

Establish the calibration graph as follows—

Measure the appropriate amounts of standard lead solution A into a series of 100-ml pear-shaped separating funnels.   For the 4-cm cell the standards should cover the range 0 to 25 μg of lead; for the 1-cm cell they should cover the range 0 to 100 μg of lead.   To each add 10 ml of distilled water followed by 2 ml of redistilled nitric acid, 2 ml of hydroxylamine hydrochloride solution, 2 ml of sodium citrate solution and 2 drops of thymol blue indicator solution, mixing the solution well; then add 10 M ammonium hydroxide until the colour of the indicator changes to full blue, and add 1 ml in excess.   Add 1 ml of potassium cyanide solution, mix and dilute the solution to 35 ml.   Extract the lead, carrying out the whole operation as described in the Procedure, beginning at "Extract the lead with dithizone extraction solution A . . ." in the third paragraph.   Measure the optical densities, using chloroform in the comparison cell.   Correct each reading for the blank and construct a graph relating the optical densities to the number of micrograms of lead.

Visual colour-comparison method—Treat the blank and test solutions similarly. Into the special titration flask (see Fig. 4) measure an aliquot of the dithizone-free solution, to contain 10 to 15 μg of lead.   Dilute the solution to 25 ml with nitric acid (1 per cent.) and adjust the solution to pH 2 by adding 2 or 3 drops of *m*-cresol purple indicator solution, followed by the addition, drop by drop, of diluted ammonium hydroxide (1 + 2) until the colour of the indicator changes to orange-pink. Add 3 ml of the ammonium hydroxide - potassium cyanide solution, followed by 10 ml of dithizone solution B, and shake for 1 minute.

Prepare a comparison standard as follows—

To 5 ml of standard lead solution B in a similar flask, add 20 ml of dilute nitric acid (1 per cent.).   Adjust the solution to pH 2 by the addition of 2 or 3 drops of *m*-cresol purple indicator solution, followed by the addition, drop by drop, of diluted ammonium hydroxide (1 + 2) until the colour of the indicator changes to orange-pink.   Add 3 ml of the ammonium hydroxide - potassium cyanide solution, followed by 10 ml of dithizone solution B, and shake for 1 minute.

Compare the colour of the chloroform layer of the test with that of the standard, and then add standard lead solution B to the solution having the lower lead content (*i.e.*, the greener solution) until, after the solutions have been shaken and the layers allowed to separate, the colours of the two chloroform layers match.   Add or subtract, as required, this added volume to or from 5·0 ml to obtain the volume of lead solution B equivalent to the lead present in the aliquot portion of the test solution taken. Correct for any lead found in the blank.

NOTE—Alternatively, the organic matter can be destroyed as described under "Preparation of Sample"; then proceed to determine the lead in a suitable aliquot of the acid solution, beginning at "Add 2 ml of hydroxylamine hydrochloride solution . . ." in the second paragraph of the Procedure.

Manganese

PRINCIPLE OF METHOD—

After destruction of the organic matter, manganese is oxidised to permanganate by means of potassium periodate in acid solution.   This is then determined colorimetrically by visual comparison with standards.   Instrumental measuring of the colour of the permanganate ion is *not* satisfactory for concentrations of the order of 0·01 to 0·05 mg per 100 ml, but visual matching in this range is easy and reproducible.

RANGE—

For manganese contents up to 0·05 mg.

APPLICABILITY—

The method is generally applicable.

REAGENTS—

NOTE—It is essential that all reagents should be of analytical-reagent quality, since the presence of organic matter must be avoided.

Distilled water—This should be specially prepared by distilling tap water to which sulphuric acid and a few crystals of potassium permanganate have been added. Suitable precautions must be taken to exclude atmospheric dust during distillation and storage.

This specially prepared water must be used for the reagents and throughout the procedure.

Potassium periodate.

Phosphoric acid, sp.gr. 1·75.

Sulphuric acid, diluted (1 + 3).

Standard manganese solution—Dissolve 0·288 g of potassium permanganate in 100 to 200 ml of distilled water, add 5 ml of diluted sulphuric acid and dilute the solution to 1 litre.

Dilute 10 ml of this solution to 100 ml with distilled water freshly as required.

1 ml ≡ 0·01 mg of manganese.

PROCEDURE—

Transfer a suitable aliquot (about 10 to 20 ml) of the acid solution, prepared as described under "Preparation of Sample," to a beaker or flask, add 1 ml of phosphoric acid and evaporate the solution on a hot-plate to fuming. Add 75 ml of the distilled water and 1 g of solid potassium periodate; cover the vessel, boil the solution for 1 minute and then immerse the vessel in a boiling-water bath for 1 hour. Cool the solution, transfer it to a 100-ml Nessler cylinder and dilute it to the 100-ml mark. Prepare a series of standards, covering the range 0·01 to 0·05 mg of manganese, by diluting suitable aliquots of the standard manganese solution to 100 ml in a series of matched Nessler cylinders. Determine the manganese content of the effluent by visual comparison with the standards.

Express the result as milligrams of manganese per litre of sample.

Mercury

PRINCIPLE OF METHOD—

In this method[1], after destruction of the organic matter by a special nitric acid - permanganate treatment under slight pressure, iron is first suppressed by hydroxylamine and the solution is made acid to eliminate other heavy metals; the mercury is then extracted with toluene as the golden brown dithizonate, which is determined colorimetrically.

RANGE—

For mercury contents up to 100 μg.

APPLICABILITY—

The method is generally applicable.

REAGENTS—

Nitric acid, sp.gr. 1·42.

Sulphuric acid, diluted (1 + 1)—Carefully add 1 volume of sulphuric acid, sp.gr. 1·84, to 1 volume of distilled water, stirring during the addition.

Hydrochloric acid, diluted (1 + 1).

Ammonium hydroxide, sp.gr. 0·880.

Potassium permanganate solution, 6 per cent. w/v

Hydroxylamine hydrochloride solution—Dissolve 25 g of hydroxylamine hydrochloride in about 60 ml of distilled water, add 0·2 ml of phenol red indicator solution, and make alkaline with ammonium hydroxide to the full red colour of the indicator. Cool and extract with a 0·01 per cent. w/v solution of dithizone in chloroform, using 5-ml portions, until the last extract remains green; then wash the solution free from excess of dithizone by repeated extraction with 10-ml portions of chloroform. Warm the solution until the excess of chloroform has been removed, cool, filter and dilute to 250 ml.

Toluene, sulphur-free, redistilled.

Dithizone stock solution—Dissolve 0·1 g of diphenylthiocarbazone (dithizone) in 100 ml of redistilled toluene.

Dithizone extraction solution—Extract 20 ml of the dithizone stock solution with two 50-ml portions of dilute ammonium hydroxide (50 ml of distilled water containing 1 ml of ammonium hydroxide) and then reject the toluene layer. Filter the combined ammoniacal extracts if necessary. Acidify the extract with diluted hydrochloric acid, and extract the precipitated dithizone with 100 ml of toluene. Wash the extract with two 10-ml portions of distilled water, and filter it through a dry filter-paper. Prepare this solution freshly each day.

Sodium hydroxide - hydroxylamine solution—Dissolve 20 g of sodium hydroxide in 500 ml of water, add 20 ml of the hydroxylamine hydrochloride solution, dilute to 1 litre and mix. Prepare this solution freshly at frequent intervals.

Standard mercury solution A—Weigh accurately 0·4 to 0·5 g of pure dry mercury into a 100-ml beaker, add 10 ml of distilled water, cover the beaker with a watch-glass and gradually add 10 ml of nitric acid, sp.gr. 1·42; warm the mixture until the mercury is completely dissolved. Add 25 ml of the diluted sulphuric acid, and evaporate the solution until white fumes of sulphur trioxide are evolved. Cool the solution and dilute it cautiously with 50 ml of distilled water, boil for 1 minute and then cool. Transfer the solution to a 500-ml calibrated flask, dilute to the mark with distilled water and mix well.

Standard mercury solution B—Measure from a 25-ml burette a volume of standard mercury solution A that will contain 0·0100 g of mercury into a 1-litre calibrated flask, add 5 ml of the diluted sulphuric acid, dilute the solution to the mark with distilled water and mix. Prepare this solution freshly as required.

$$1 \text{ ml} \equiv 10 \ \mu\text{g of mercury.}$$

Phenol red indicator solution.

PROCEDURE—

Transfer 50 ml of the effluent sample to a glass pressure bottle, having a capacity of about 300 ml, that can be heated and will withstand a pressure slightly above that of the atmosphere. Add 20 ml of concentrated nitric acid and 20 ml of potassium permanganate solution; gently mix the solution and stopper the bottle. Place it in a suitable beaker having a capacity of about 600 ml and containing sufficient water to come well above the level of the solution in the pressure bottle; put the beaker on top of a boiling-water bath and heat it for 2 hours. Then remove the bottle and cool it thoroughly. Shake the bottle and invert it so that the solution will come into contact with the contained vapour. Carefully remove the stopper, covering the bottle with a towel during the removal.*   Rinse the stopper with distilled water, adding the rinsings to the contents of the bottle.

If, at this stage, excess of permanganate is not present, add potassium permanganate solution, 1 ml at a time, until an excess remains when the solution has been standing for 2 minutes after the addition.   Remove the excess of permanganate by the addition of hydroxylamine hydrochloride solution.   Add a few drops of phenol red indicator solution and then ammonium hydroxide until the solution attains the full red colour of the indicator, keeping the solution cool during the addition.   Add 20 ml of diluted sulphuric acid and then 10 ml of hydroxylamine hydrochloride solution; transfer the solution to a 250-ml calibrated flask, cool, dilute to the mark and mix.   Allow the solution to stand for at least 3 hours, or overnight.

Transfer a suitable aliquot of the solution (usually 100 ml), containing not more than 100 μg of mercury, to a 250-ml pear-shaped separating funnel.   Add 3 ml of dithizone extraction solution and 7 ml of toluene, and then shake the mixture vigorously for 30 seconds.   Allow the layers to separate and observe the colour of the dithizone in the toluene layer; excess of dithizone is indicated by a green or brownish-green colour.   If the colour of the toluene layer is golden brown, continue the addition of the dithizone extraction solution, 0·5 ml at a time, with shaking, as directed above, until an excess is present as indicated by the appearance of a green tint.   Note the total volume of dithizone extraction solution used.   Allow the layers to separate, discard the aqueous (lower) layer, wash the toluene layer once with 10 ml of distilled water without shaking and reject the washing.

Add 10 ml of diluted hydrochloric acid and shake the mixture vigorously for half a minute.   Allow the layers to separate, run the lower layer into a second separating funnel and wash the toluene - dithizone layer twice without shaking, using 50 ml of distilled water for each washing.   Add the washings to the acid extract contained in the second funnel.   Reject the toluene layer.

To the acid extract and washings add 5 ml of hydroxylamine hydrochloride solution, a volume of dithizone extraction solution equal to that used in the initial extraction and 7 ml of toluene; then shake the mixture thoroughly for half a minute. Allow the layers to separate and reject the aqueous layer.   Wash the toluene - dithizone layer once with 10 ml of distilled water without shaking and reject the washing.

Remove excess of dithizone by the addition of 10 ml of sodium hydroxide - hydroxylamine solution, shake the mixture for half a minute and allow the layers to separate.   Reject the aqueous layer.   Repeat the sodium hydroxide - hydroxylamine extraction twice more, rejecting the aqueous layer each time.   The toluene layer is golden brown in colour when mercury is present.   Separate the last aqueous layer as completely as possible, discard it and dry the bore of the stem of the separating funnel with a strip of filter-paper.   Filter the toluene - mercury dithizonate solution through a dry 9-cm Whatman No. 41 filter-paper containing about 0·5 g of anhydrous sodium sulphate, and collect the dry filtrate in a 25-ml calibrated flask.   Rinse the separating funnel a few times with small volumes of toluene, pass the rinsings through the same filter-paper and collect them in the flask.   Dilute the combined filtrates with toluene to the mark and mix the solution.

Carry out a blank procedure on all the reagents used.

Measure the optical densities of the test and blank solutions in a spectrophotometer or in an absorptiometer, using a 4-cm or a 1-cm cell according to the depth of colour, and using a wavelength of 4800 A in a spectrophotometer or a suitable blue filter in an absorptiometer.   Use toluene in the comparison cell.   Read the numbers of micrograms of mercury equivalent to the observed optical densities of

* In the presence of chloride in an amount greater than the equivalent of 1 per cent. of sodium chloride, chlorine will have been liberated and care should be taken in handling the bottle.

the test and blank solutions from a previously prepared calibration graph and so obtain the net measure of mercury in the sample.

Express the result as milligrams of mercury per litre of sample.

Establish the calibration graph as follows—

Measure appropriate amounts of the standard mercury solution B, covering the range 0 to 100 μg of mercury, into a series of 250-ml pear-shaped separating funnels. To each add 7 ml of diluted sulphuric acid, and dilute each solution to 100 ml; then add 5 ml of hydroxylamine hydrochloride solution and extract the mercury with toluene - dithizone solution as described above, beginning at "Add 3 ml of dithizone extraction solution . . ." in the third paragraph. Measure the optical densities, using a 4-cm cell to cover the range 0 to 30 μg of mercury and a 1-cm cell to cover the range 30 to 100 μg, and construct a graph relating the optical densities to the number of micrograms of mercury.

REFERENCE

1. Rolfe, A. C., Russell, F. R. and Wilkinson, N. T., *Analyst*, 1955, **80**, 523.

Nickel

PRINCIPLE OF METHOD—

After destruction of the organic matter, nickel is extracted from the ammoniacal solution as its dimethylglyoxime complex and is finally determined as the nickelic complex.

RANGE—

For nickel contents up to 100 μg.

APPLICABILITY—

The method is generally applicable.

REAGENTS—

Hydrochloric acid, sp.gr. 1·18.

Ammonium hydroxide, sp.gr. 0·880.

Chloroform—Shake 500 ml of chloroform with 50 ml of 10 per cent. w/v hydrochloric acid. Allow the layers to separate, run the chloroform into another separating funnel and wash it in a similar manner with distilled water until it is free from acid.

Sodium citrate solution, 25 per cent. w/v.

Bromine water, saturated.

Sodium dimethylglyoxime solution—A 0·2 per cent. w/v solution in dilute ammonium hydroxide $(1 + 19)$.

Hydrochloric acid, dilute $(1 + 19)$.

Standard nickel solution—Dissolve 0·0479 g of nickel sulphate, $NiSO_4.7H_2O$, in distilled water containing 1 ml of N sulphuric acid and dilute the solution to 1 litre. Prepare this solution freshly as required.

1 ml $\equiv$ 10 μg of nickel.

PROCEDURE—

Measure a suitable aliquot of the solution prepared as described under "Preparation of Sample" and dilute it to 100 ml. Add 10 ml of the sodium citrate solution. Place a small piece of litmus paper in the solution and add ammonium hydroxide, with mixing, until the solution is just ammoniacal; then add 10 drops in excess. Transfer the solution to a 250-ml separating funnel.

Add 10 ml of sodium dimethylglyoxime solution and shake the mixture for 1 minute; then allow it to stand for 10 minutes. Add 10 ml of chloroform, shake for 1 minute and allow the layers to separate. Run the chloroform layer into another separating funnel and rinse the stem of the first with about 3 ml of chloroform, adding the rinsings to the first chloroform extract. Repeat the extraction of the aqueous layer with a further 10 ml of chloroform, and add this chloroform extract to the first, rinsing the stem of the funnel as before.

To the combined chloroform extracts add 15 ml of dilute hydrochloric acid and shake the mixture vigorously for 1 minute. Allow the layers to separate. Run the chloroform layer into another separating funnel and carry out a further washing of the chloroform with 5 ml of dilute hydrochloric acid. Reject the chloroform layer. Combine the two acid extracts and transfer the solution to a 100-ml beaker. Rinse the two separating funnels that contained the acid extracts with a few millilitres of distilled water and add the rinsings to the acid extract in the beaker. Heat the solution very carefully over a low Bunsen flame to expel any chloroform. Continue to boil the solution until the volume is approximately 25 ml. Cool the solution, transfer it to a 50-ml calibrated flask and rinse the beaker twice, using 5 ml of distilled water for each rinsing. Add, in the following order, mixing after each addition—

(a) 2 ml of sodium citrate solution,
(b) 2 ml of bromine water,
(c) just enough ammonium hydroxide to destroy the bromine colour and to give a 1-ml excess, and
(d) 4 ml of sodium dimethylglyoxime solution.

Dilute the solution to the mark with distilled water and mix well.

Carry out a blank procedure on all the reagents used.

Measure the optical densities of the test and blank solutions in a spectrophotometer or in an absorptiometer, using a 4-cm cell, and using a wavelength of 4800 A in a spectrophotometer or a suitable blue filter in an absorptiometer. Use water in the comparison cell. Read the number of micrograms of nickel equivalent to the observed optical densities of the test and blank solutions from a previously prepared calibration graph, and so obtain the net measure of nickel in the sample.

Express the result as milligrams of nickel per litre of sample.

Establish the calibration graph as follows—

Measure appropriate amounts of standard nickel solution to cover the range 0 to 100 μg into a series of 50-ml calibrated flasks. Add to each 20 ml of dilute hydrochloric acid and the reagents (a) to (d) as described above. Dilute each solution to the mark, mix well, measure the optical densities and construct a graph relating the optical densities to the number of micrograms of nickel.

If an instrument is not available, colours may be matched visually against a series of standards.

Potassium

The determination should be carried out by flame photometric methods. Since commercial instruments vary it is not practicable here to give detailed instructions for preparation of the sample, etc., and the makers' instructions should be followed. Further information is given in the Appendix, p. 122.

Express the result as milligrams of potassium per litre of sample.

Selenium

Two methods are given—the first is a "sorting" test to establish the presence of selenium in a trade waste and to give an approximation of its content; the second

F

is the recommended method of determination.[1] Visual colour measurement is recommended in both methods. Instrumental measuring is *not* recommended; the solution is colloidal, and although the colour can be matched either visually or nephelometrically, visual matching is to be preferred.

TEST TO ESTABLISH THE PRESENCE OF SELENIUM AND TO MEASURE THE APPROXIMATE CONTENT

PRINCIPLE OF METHOD—

After destruction of the organic matter, the selenium present in the effluent is reduced by means of either hydrazine sulphate or ascorbic acid to the elemental form, which is measured colorimetrically against standards.

RANGE—

For selenium contents up to 1·0 mg.

APPLICABILITY—

The method is generally applicable.

REAGENTS—

Hydrochloric acid, diluted (1 + 1),
Hydrazine sulphate,
    or
Ascorbic acid.
Standard selenium solution—Dissolve 1 g of selenium in nitric acid, sp.gr. 1·42, and dilute the solution to 100 ml with distilled water. Measure a 10-ml aliquot into a beaker and add 5 ml of sulphuric acid, sp.gr. 1·84. Evaporate the solution until copious white fumes of sulphur trioxide are evolved. Cool and then add 5 ml of distilled water and repeat the evaporation. Cool the liquid and dilute with distilled water to 500 ml in a calibrated flask.

$$1 \text{ ml} \equiv 0.2 \text{ mg of selenium.}$$

PROCEDURE—

Destroy the organic matter in a volume of the effluent sample containing from 1 to 10 mg of selenium by wet oxidation, as described under "Preparation of Sample," but omitting the addition of ammonium oxalate used in removing the excess of nitric acid. Dilute the filtrate to 100 ml with distilled water. Measure an aliquot not exceeding 10 ml into a large boiling-tube; if a smaller volume than 10 ml is taken, dilute it to 10 ml with distilled water in the tube. Add 30 ml of diluted hydrochloric acid and heat the tube in a water bath maintained at 40° to 45° C until the temperature of the test liquid reaches 40° C; then add either (a) 0·25 g of hydrazine sulphate, or (b) 0·4 g of solid ascorbic acid, and mix. Maintain the temperature of the liquid at 40° to 45° C for 30 minutes. Simultaneously measure 1, 2, 3, 4 and 5 ml of the standard selenium solution into a series of boiling-tubes, dilute each to 10 ml, add 30 ml of hydrochloric acid and either hydrazine or ascorbic acid as before. Maintain the tubes containing the standards at the same temperature as the tube containing the test liquid for 30 minutes. Cool the solutions, transfer them to Nessler cylinders and dilute to 50 ml with distilled water. Match the sample with the standards.

Express the result as milligrams of selenium per litre of sample.

RECOMMENDED METHOD OF DETERMINATION

PRINCIPLE OF METHOD—

After destruction of the organic matter by wet oxidation, the selenium in the effluent is distilled as the bromide, which in the aqueous distillate becomes selenious acid. This is reduced to elemental selenium by means of ascorbic acid and measured colorimetrically against standards.

RANGE—

For selenium contents up to 0·25 mg.

APPLICABILITY—

The method is generally applicable.

REAGENTS—

Nitric acid, sp.gr. 1·42.
Sulphuric acid, sp.gr. 1·84.
Perchloric acid, 60 *per cent.*
Sodium hydroxide solution, 1·0 N.
Hydrobromic acid, redistilled—Purify hydrobromic acid by distillation. Collect the colourless middle fraction of the distillate. Determine the hydrogen bromide content of the collected fraction by titrating 5 ml with *N* sodium hydroxide solution, using methyl orange as indicator.
Hydrobromic acid - bromine reagent—Mix 3 ml of bromine with 197 ml of hydrobromic acid.
Standard selenium solution A—Weigh 1·405 g of selenium dioxide and dissolve it in distilled water. Transfer the solution to a 1-litre calibrated flask, add 80 ml of hydrobromic acid and dilute the solution to the mark; mix well.
Standard selenium solution B—Measure 10 ml of selenium solution A into a 100-ml calibrated flask, add 1 ml of hydrobromic acid and dilute the solution to the mark; mix well. Prepare this solution freshly as required.

$$1 \text{ ml} \equiv 0 \cdot 1 \text{ mg of selenium.}$$

Ascorbic acid.
Methyl orange indicator solution—A 0·04 per cent. solution in 20 per cent. ethanol.

PROCEDURE—

Measure a suitable volume of the effluent sample into a beaker. Acidify the solution by the addition of nitric acid and add 5 ml in excess; then add 1·0 ml of perchloric acid. Evaporate the solution to about 10 ml and then cool it. Add 5 ml of sulphuric acid and heat the solution on a sand-bath until white fumes appear. If all the organic matter is not completely destroyed at this stage, cautiously add a further 1 ml of nitric acid and heat the solution again until white fumes appear. Allow the solution to cool; then add 10 ml of distilled water and heat the solution until white fumes appear. Repeat the treatment with distilled water and the evaporation a second time.

Cool the solution and transfer it to a 300-ml distillation flask, using 25 ml of distilled water for the transfer of the solution to the flask. Add 50 ml of hydro-bromic acid and 6 ml of hydrobromic acid - bromine reagent. Then slowly and carefully add 25 ml of sulphuric acid to the contents of the flask, cooling the flask during the addition. Place a boiling-rod inside the distillation flask. Fit an adaptor and water-cooled condenser to the flask and place a 100-ml conical flask, marked at 80 ml and containing 4 ml of hydrobromic acid - bromine reagent, at the condenser outlet; tilt the conical flask so that the tip of the condenser lies below the level of the reagent.

Heat the contents of the distillation flask, gently at first until the solution is boiling and afterwards more strongly, and allow the distillation to proceed until the volume of solution in the receiver is 80 ml. Remove the receiver and discontinue the distillation. Transfer the distillate to a 100-ml calibrated flask, dilute the solution to the mark with distilled water and mix.

PREPARATION OF STANDARD SELENIUM DISTILLATE—

Measure into a distillation flask similar to that used for the sample solution 25 ml of standard selenium solution B, and follow the same procedure for the distillation of selenium as described above, beginning with the addition of 50 ml of hydrobromic acid. Allow the distillation to proceed until the volume of solution in the receiver is 80 ml. Transfer the distillate to a 100-ml calibrated flask and dilute the solution to the mark with distilled water and mix well.

COLORIMETRIC DETERMINATION—

Determine the acidity of the sample and standard distillate solutions on an aliquot of each solution as follows—

Measure 5 ml of the solution, add 100 ml of distilled water and boil the solution until it is free from bromine, but do not reduce the volume below 50 ml. Cool the solution, add 2 drops of methyl orange indicator solution and titrate with $1\cdot0\ N$ sodium hydroxide solution.

Measure aliquots of the standard distillate solution into a series of 50-ml Nessler cylinders, covering the range 0 to 0·25 mg of selenium in steps of 0·025 mg. From the results of the titrations calculate the volume of hydrobromic acid that must be put into each cylinder to make the acid content of each standard the same as that of 50 ml of sample distillate solution. Add these volumes and then dilute each standard to 50 ml with distilled water.

Measure 50 ml of the sample distillate solution into a 50-ml Nessler cylinder. Precipitate the selenium in the test and standard solutions by adding 0·4 g of ascorbic acid to each solution; stir the solutions until the ascorbic acid has dissolved. Allow the solutions to stand for 30 minutes and then visually match the coloured turbidity in the sample solution against the coloured turbidities in the standard solutions.

NOTE—The free bromine content of the sample and standard solutions will be different, but experience has shown that the shade and intensity of the coloured turbidity is not affected by any variation in the free bromine content of the selenium solution that occurs under the conditions described.

Express the result as milligrams of selenium per litre of sample.

REFERENCE

1. Fogg, D. N., and Wilkinson, N. T., *Analyst*, 1956, **81**, 525.

Sodium

The determination should be carried out by flame photometric methods. Since commercial instruments vary it is not practicable here to give detailed instructions for preparation of the sample, etc., and the makers' instructions should be followed. Further information is given in the Appendix, p. 122.

Express the result as milligrams of sodium per litre of sample.

Zinc

Two methods are recommended, depending on the amount of zinc present in the sample.

ZINC CONTENTS GREATER THAN 5 mg PER LITRE

PRINCIPLE OF METHOD—

In this method,[1] after destruction of the organic matter, zinc (together with certain other heavy metals) is extracted at pH 4·5 with a solution of dithizone in chloroform. Zinc, together with bismuth and cadmium, is then extracted from the chloroform phase with dilute hydrochloric acid. After evaporation of the acid extract, the zinc in the residue is treated with potassium iodide in the presence of potassium ferricyanide. The iodine that is quantitatively liberated is then titrated with thiosulphate. This reaction is specific for zinc.

RANGE—

For zinc contents greater than 5 mg per litre of sample.

APPLICABILITY—

The method is generally applicable.

REAGENTS—

Ammonium acetate solution—Dissolve 386 g of ammonium acetate in distilled water and dilute to 1 litre.

Dithizone solution in chloroform—Dissolve, without heating, 0·15 g of diphenyl-thiocarbazone (dithizone) in 100 ml of chloroform in a separating funnel. Free the solution from copper as follows—

To the solution contained in the separating funnel add 100 ml of distilled water and 5 ml of ammonium hydroxide, sp.gr. 0·880, and shake the mixture vigorously. Discard the chloroform layer and wash the alkaline liquid with two 5-ml portions of chloroform. Add 200 ml of analytical-reagent grade chloroform and then hydrochloric acid until the aqueous layer is colourless on shaking. Run off the chloroform solution and store it in a brown-glass bottle.

Hydrochloric acid, diluted (1 + 1).

Hydrochloric acid, dilute (1 + 10).

Acetic acid, glacial.

Potassium ferricyanide solution, 1 *per cent. w/v*—Prepare this solution freshly as required.

Potassium iodide solution, 5 *per cent. w/v*—Prepare this solution freshly as required.

Ammonium hydrogen fluoride.

Perchloric acid, 60 *per cent. w/v.*

Hydrogen peroxide, 30 *per cent. w/v* (100-volume).

Sodium thiosulphate solution, 0·1 N.

Sodium thiosulphate solution, 0·002 N—Make an appropriate dilution of the 0·1 N solution with freshly boiled and cooled distilled water. Prepare this solution freshly each day and store in the dark

Starch indicator solution, 1 *per cent. w/v.*

PROCEDURE—

Transfer to a separating funnel a suitable volume (containing preferably 0·1 to 1·0 mg of zinc, but not exceeding 40 ml) of the acid solution, prepared as described under "Preparation of Sample," and add 10 ml of ammonium acetate solution.

Add 5 ml of dithizone solution and shake the mixture vigorously. Allow the layers to separate* and transfer the chloroform extract to a second separating funnel, leaving the aqueous layer in the first funnel. Wash the chloroform extract by shaking it with a mixture of 6 ml of ammonium acetate solution, 3 ml of diluted hydrochloric acid (1 + 1) and 10 ml of distilled water. Allow the layers to separate, transfer the chloroform layer to a third separating funnel, and wash it with 20 ml of distilled

---

* If a reddish purple colour does not appear in the chloroform layer, there is too little zinc present for this method to be applied.

water. Transfer the chloroform layer to a fourth separating funnel, leaving the wash waters in the second and third funnels.

Again extract the liquid remaining in the first funnel with another 5 ml of dithizone solution, and follow the same washing procedure, using the wash liquids left in the funnels from the treatment of the previous extract. If necessary, repeat the process until the zinc has been completely extracted from the liquid in the first funnel, as indicated by the colour of the dithizone solution remaining unchanged after shaking.

To the combined dithizone - chloroform extracts collected in the fourth separating funnel add 10 ml of dilute hydrochloric acid $(1 + 10)$. After shaking, run the chloroform layer into another funnel and transfer the acid solution to a 60-ml or 100-ml borosilicate-glass beaker. Wash the funnel that contained the chloroform solution with about 10 ml of distilled water, adding the washing to the contents of the beaker. Re-extract the dithizone solution with another 10 ml of dilute hydrochloric acid $(1 + 10)$ and again wash the funnel with 10 ml of distilled water, adding the acid extract and washing to the liquid in the beaker.

Evaporate the contents of the beaker to dryness. Add to the residue 5 drops of perchloric acid and 5 drops of hydrogen peroxide, and evaporate to dryness on a hot-plate. Repeat the treatment until all organic matter has been destroyed and a white residue remains. Wash down the sides of the beaker with distilled water and again evaporate to dryness.

To the residue add 0·1 ml of glacial acetic acid and a "speck" (about 0·01 g) of ammonium hydrogen fluoride, and then 2 ml of potassium iodide solution and 2 drops of starch indicator solution. If a blue colour appears after the addition of the starch, add 0·002 N sodium thiosulphate solution until the colour is just discharged. Add about 0·5 ml of potassium ferricyanide solution to the mixture, stirring it with a glass rod, and titrate with 0·002 N sodium thiosulphate solution. (If possible the titration should be carried out by artificial light, but this is not essential.) The blue starch - iodide complex may be adsorbed on the precipitated zinc ferrocyanide, and if this occurs the precipitate serves as an indicator.

Express the result as milligrams of zinc per litre of sample.

NOTE—The end-point is usually quite definite: the blue starch - iodide colour returns after a few minutes, but this should be ignored.

1 ml of 0·002 N sodium thiosulphate solution $\equiv$ 0·196 mg of zinc.

ZINC CONTENTS UP TO 5 mg PER LITRE

The method of determination recommended by the Society[2] is known to give accurate results for very small amounts of zinc, but it is not recommended as a routine method for trade effluents because of its complexity.

PRINCIPLE OF METHOD—

After destruction of the organic matter, copper is removed if necessary and zinc is separated from other metals by extraction with dithizone at pH 4·7. Excess of dithizone is removed with sodium sulphide and the zinc - dithizone complex in carbon tetrachloride is then measured colorimetrically.

RANGE—

For zinc contents up to 5 mg per litre of sample.

APPLICABILITY—

The method is generally applicable.

REAGENTS—

Distilled water—For preparing all the reagents, use distilled water that has been twice redistilled from glass. It is recommended that the distilled water be stored in polythene bottles.

Hydrochloric acid, 1·0 N

Carbon tetrachloride, redistilled.

Dithizone stock solution—Dissolve 0·05 g of diphenylthiocarbazone (dithizone) in 100 ml of redistilled carbon tetrachloride.

Dithizone extraction solution—Extract 10 ml of the dithizone stock solution with two 50-ml portions of dilute ammonium hydroxide (50 ml of distilled water containing 2 ml of 10 M ammonium hydroxide) and then reject the carbon tetrachloride layer. Filter the combined ammoniacal extracts if necessary. Acidify the extract with dilute hydrochloric acid (about 1 per cent.) and extract the precipitated dithizone with 100 ml of carbon tetrachloride. Wash the extract with two 10-ml portions of distilled water, and filter it through a dry filter-paper.

Prepare this solution freshly as required.

Sodium acetate - acetic acid buffer solution—Dissolve 136 g of sodium acetate, $CH_3COONa.3H_2O$, and 58 ml of glacial acetic acid in distilled water, and dilute to 500 ml. Extract this solution with small portions of a 0·05 per cent. w/v dithizone solution in carbon tetrachloride, shaking the mixture for about 2 minutes each time. Repeat the extraction until the final extract is pure green in colour. Filter the solution through cotton-wool to remove any carbon tetrachloride.

Sodium thiosulphate solution, 25 per cent. w/v.

Sodium sulphide solution, 0·04 per cent. w/v—Dissolve 4 g of analytical-reagent grade sodium sulphide, $Na_2S.9H_2O$, in distilled water and dilute to 100 ml. Dilute 1 ml of this solution to 100 ml. Prepare this solution freshly as required.

Sodium sulphate, anhydrous.

Standard zinc solution—Dissolve 0·4398 g of zinc sulphate, $ZnSO_4.7H_2O$, in distilled water, dilute to 1 litre and mix well. Dilute 10·0 ml of this solution to 1 litre. Prepare this solution freshly as required.

$$1 \text{ ml} \equiv 1 \ \mu g \text{ of zinc.}$$

PROCEDURE—

Determine the acidity of a 10-ml portion of the acid solution prepared as described under "Preparation of Sample." Adjust the acidity of a suitable portion (containing not more than 5 μg of zinc) of the acid solution to 0·1 N; note the volume of the adjusted solution.

Add 5·0 ml of dithizone extraction solution, shake the mixture for 2 minutes, and then allow the layers to separate. Observe the colour of the dithizone in the carbon tetrachloride layer; excess of dithizone is indicated by a green or brownish green colour. If the colour of the carbon tetrachloride layer is red, continue the addition of dithizone extraction solution, 0·5 ml at a time, with shaking, as directed above, until an excess is present, as indicated by the appearance of a green tint. Allow the layers to separate and discard the dithizone layer containing the copper complex. Repeat this extraction with dithizone extraction solution twice more, discarding the dithizone layer each time.

To the aqueous solution remaining in the separating funnel add half its volume of the sodium acetate - acetic acid buffer solution, mix and then add 1·0 ml of sodium thiosulphate solution. Add 4·0 ml of dithizone extraction solution, measured from a burette, shake the mixture for 2 minutes and allow the layers to separate. Transfer the lower layer to a second separating funnel, filtering it through a small plug of cotton-wool. Wash the aqueous layer with 1 ml of carbon tetrachloride and filter the carbon tetrachloride through the cotton-wool plug.   Repeat the extraction procedure a second time, when the dithizone layer will be green if the zinc content does not exceed 5 μg and if the dithizone extraction solution is of satisfactory concentration. (This can easily be checked by extracting a known amount of zinc with the dithizone solution.)   Filter the second extract through the same cotton-wool plug into the second separating funnel.   Wash the aqueous layer with 1 ml of carbon tetrachloride as before.   Shake the combined dithizone - carbon tetrachloride extracts for 10 seconds with 10 ml of sodium sulphide solution to remove excess of dithizone. Allow the layers to separate and transfer the lower layer to a third separating funnel. Wash the aqueous layer in the second funnel with 1 ml of carbon tetrachloride and add this to the main solution.   Extract the carbon tetrachloride solution with further 10-ml portions of sodium sulphide solution until the aqueous layer is no longer yellow.   Shake the carbon tetrachloride layer with about 1 g of anhydrous sodium sulphate and filter it through a dry 9-cm filter-paper (Whatman No. 41) into a 25-ml calibrated flask.   Wash the funnel and the filter-paper with a few millilitres of carbon tetrachloride, adding the washings to the solution in the flask, and dilute the solution to the mark with carbon tetrachloride.

Carry out a blank procedure on all the reagents used.

Measure the optical densities of the test and blank solutions in a spectrophotometer or in an absorptiometer, using a 1-cm cell and using a wavelength of 5320 A in a spectrophotometer or a suitable green filter in an absorptiometer.   Use carbon tetrachloride in the comparison cell.   Read the number of micrograms of zinc equivalent to the observed optical densities of the test and blank solutions from a previously prepared calibration graph and so obtain the net measure of zinc in the sample.

Express the result as milligrams of zinc per litre of sample.

Establish the calibration graph as follows—

Measure appropriate amounts of standard zinc solution covering the range 0 to 5 μg of zinc into a series of separating funnels and add to each 1 ml of 1·0 N hydrochloric acid and dilute the solution to 10 ml.   Add 5 ml of the sodium acetate - acetic acid buffer solution and 1·0 ml of sodium thiosulphate solution.   Extract the zinc as described above, beginning at "Add 4·0 ml of dithizone extraction solution, measured from a burette, . . ." in the third paragraph, taking care that the treatment with sodium sulphide solution is exactly the same as in the test, i.e., as regards duration of shaking, etc. Measure the optical densities, using a 1-cm cell, and construct a graph relating the optical densities to the number of micrograms of zinc.

REFERENCES

1. Sylvester, N. D., and Hughes, E. B., *Analyst*, 1936, **61**, 734.
2. Analytical Methods Committee, *Analyst*, 1948, **73**, 304.

Non-metallic Contaminants

Organic Carbon

There is no one general method for the determination of organic carbon; the methods used include modifications designed to eliminate errors arising from the presence of one or more types of compound in the sample. A dry-combustion method cannot be used for sewage and sewage effluent, since loss of organic carbon would occur during the preparation of the sample. In the wet oxidation with hot chromic and sulphuric acids, used in the methods described below, volatile organic compounds, oxalates and thiocyanates may all cause errors unless special precautions are taken to ensure complete oxidation.

The method recommended is a modification of that described by Mills[1] for sewage, a combustion tube being introduced to ensure complete oxidation. The method is, therefore, applicable to sewage, sewage effluents and the majority of trade wastes. When interfering substances are known to be absent, the method may be simplified by omission of the combustion tube.

METHOD A: INTERFERING SUBSTANCES (*e.g.*, VOLATILE ORGANIC COMPOUNDS,
OXALATES AND THIOCYANATES) NOT KNOWN TO BE ABSENT

REAGENTS—

Sulphuric acid, sp.gr. 1·84—It may be convenient to mix together several batches of acid. The number of blank determinations is thereby reduced.

Chromic acid—A saturated solution of chromium trioxide in distilled water.

Barium hydroxide, approximately 0·1 N*—Dissolve 18 g of barium hydroxide, $Ba(OH)_2.8H_2O$, of analytical-reagent quality, or 20 g of the commercial grade, in 1 litre of distilled water in a flask. Insert the stopper and then shake the flask until all the crystals have dissolved. Allow the solution to stand for 2 days or until all the carbonate has settled. Siphon the clear solution into a storage bottle connected to a 25-ml automatic pipette. Exclude carbon dioxide by attaching soda-lime guard tubes.

Hydrochloric acid, exactly 0·1 N*—Dilute 10 ml of hydrochloric acid, sp.gr. 1·18, to 1 litre with distilled water. Standardise against pure dry sodium carbonate and dilute to exactly 0·1 N.

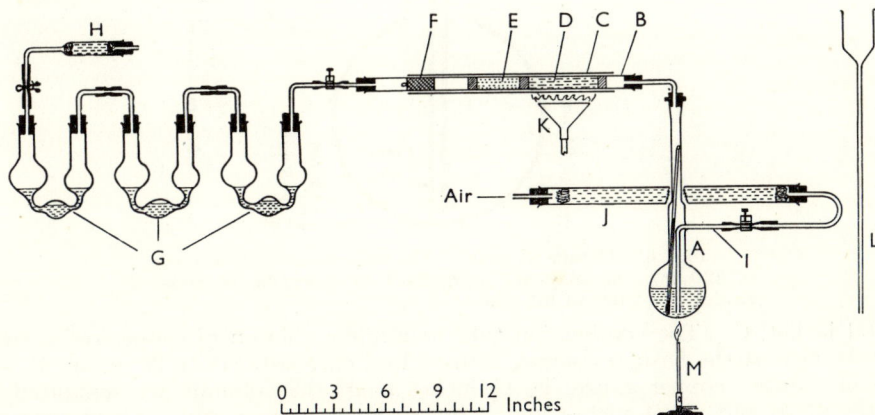

Fig. 5. Apparatus for the determination of organic carbon

* If it is desired to use barium hydroxide solution and hydrochloric acid such that
1 ml ≡ 1 mg of carbon,
use 30 g (33 g of the commercial grade) and 15 ml, respectively, for preparing the solutions.

Phenolphthalein indicator solution—Dissolve 0·1 g of phenolphthalein in 50 ml of industrial methylated spirit and dilute to 100 ml with distilled water.

APPARATUS—

The apparatus is shown diagrammatically in Fig. 5. The flask A (Fig. 6), which has a capacity of 250 ml, has a fused-in side-arm reaching almost to the bottom of the bulb and a neck 9 inches long and with an internal diameter of approximately ½ inch. The neck of the flask is connected, preferably by a ground-glass joint, to a combustion tube, B, 16 inches long and with an internal diameter of ½ inch. The tube is wrapped in asbestos paper and surrounded for two-thirds of its length by

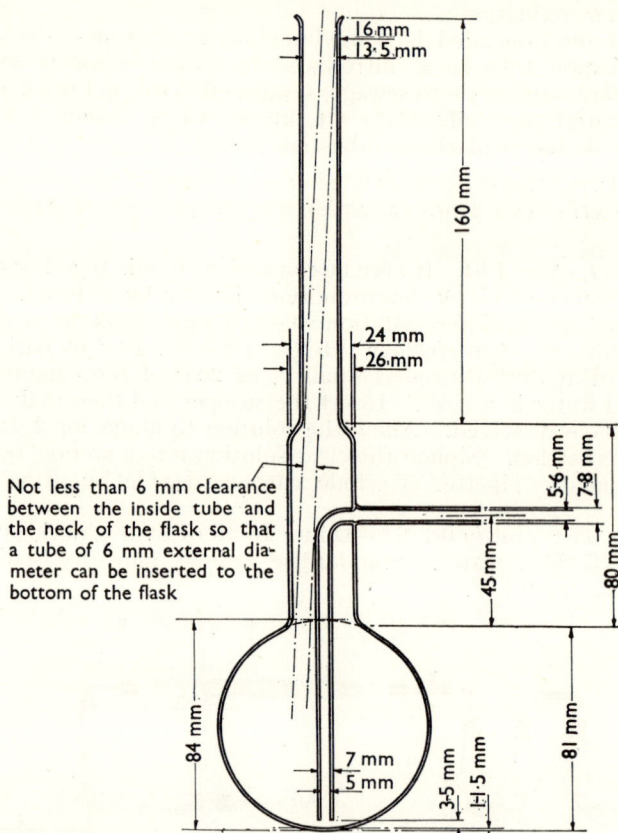

Fig. 6. Details of flask. The total volume of the flask is 320 ml; the material used must be borosilicate glass. Scale: one-third of full size

a metal jacket, C. The combustion tube contains a column of copper oxide (wire form), D, nearest the flask, a column of fused lead chromate (14 to 20 mesh), E, and a roll of reduced copper gauze, F, 1½ inches long; the columns are separated by asbestos plugs and are 4 inches and 3 inches long, respectively. Three specially made absorption tubes,* G (see Fig. 7), and a soda-lime tube, H, are connected in

---

* Other types of absorption tubes could be used, but existing tubes sold commercially would have the disadvantage that either the contents would have to be washed out for titration or the volume of absorbent and the "dead space" would be greater and thus larger errors might arise.

series to the other end of the combustion tube. The side-arm, I, of the flask, A, is connected to a source of air free from carbon dioxide. This may be obtained by passing air through a long tube, J, packed with granules of soda-lime. A burner, K, is arranged beneath the jacketed part of the combustion tube so that the column of copper oxide is the most strongly heated. If the lead chromate is too strongly heated, it will fuse together as one mass.

If large amounts of chloride (up to about 5000 mg of Cl′ per litre) are present in the sample, a bubbler containing distilled water should be inserted between flask A and the combustion tube. If the content of chloride is greater than about 5000 mg of Cl′ per litre, uncontrollable evolution of vapours occurs when the reagents are mixed with the sample and accurate results cannot then be obtained.

Reduction of the copper gauze—The copper gauze must be reduced before each determination. Heat the roll of gauze to redness in a bunsen flame and drop it into a borosilicate-glass test-tube containing about 1 ml of methanol. Insert the stopper in the tube and allow the gauze to cool before removing it.

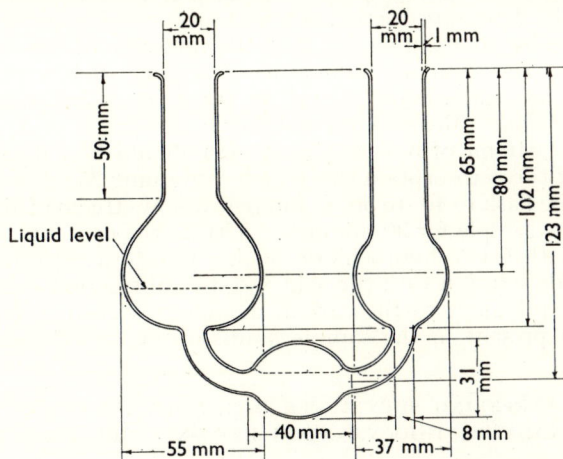

Fig. 7. Details of absorption tube. The total volume of the tube is 172 ml, and the approximate levels of the liquid when the tube is being used and contains 25 ml of absorbent are shown by the dotted lines. Scale: one-third of full size

PROCEDURE—

Total carbon—Into each absorption tube measure 25·0 ml of barium hydroxide solution. Connect the tubes in series and close the ends with clips, but do not yet attach them to the combustion tube. Light the burner under the combustion tube and pass a slow stream of air free from carbon dioxide through the flask and combustion tube for at least 30 minutes. Stop the flow of air, connect the absorption tubes to the combustion tube and open the clips. Transfer into the flask a suitable volume of the effluent sample, not more than 50 ml and containing not more than 20 mg of organic carbon. Add 150 ml of sulphuric acid by means of the long-stemmed funnel, L (Fig. 5), so that it forms a layer beneath the sample. Into the flask measure with a safety pipette 10 ml of saturated chromic acid solution, put in a 0° to 200° C thermometer, and immediately re-connect the flask to the combustion tube. Light the micro-burner, M, beneath the flask and gently shake the flask to mix the contents. As the temperature in the flask is raised, evolution of gas occurs, and during this stage the heating should be adjusted so that the current of gas does not overload the absorption tubes. Allow the temperature in the flask to rise to 145° to 155° C and then adjust the burner so that the temperature is kept within these limits for 2 hours. At the end of this period the contents of the flask should be deep green in colour. The contents of the flask should never be heated so strongly that white fumes of sulphur trioxide are formed.

Stop heating the flask and pass air free from carbon dioxide through the liquid for 30 minutes, at a rate of about two to three bubbles per second, to sweep out any residual carbon dioxide. Titrate the contents of each absorption tube with 0·1 N hydrochloric acid, using phenolphthalein as indicator. Subtract the sum of the titres of the test from the *sum* of the titres obtained from a similar blank experiment from which the sample is omitted. This gives the volume of standard hydrochloric acid equivalent to the total amount of carbon originally present in the sample as dissolved carbon dioxide, bicarbonate, carbonate and organic carbon.

1 ml of 0·1 N hydrochloric acid $\equiv$ 0·6 mg of carbon.

The total amount of carbon present as carbon dioxide, bicarbonate and carbonate must next be determined separately and subtracted from the total determined as described above by combustion, so that the quantity of the organic carbon can be found. Express the result as milligrams of organic carbon per litre of sample.

Determination of total carbon present in the form of dissolved carbon dioxide, bicarbonate and carbonate—Measure into another flask, similar to A, 200 ml of sample. Acidify the sample (10 ml of 5 N sulphuric acid should be sufficient) and connect the flask to a set of three absorption tubes each containing 25 ml of barium hydroxide solution. Warm the flask to 40° to 50° C and pass a slow stream of air free from carbon dioxide through the sample for 30 minutes. Titrate the contents of each absorption tube, as before, with 0·1 N hydrochloric acid. Titrate a separate 25-ml quantity of barium hydroxide solution with the acid and, by subtraction, calculate the volume of standard acid equivalent to the carbon dioxide absorbed. Hence calculate the amount of carbon present in the sample as dissolved carbon dioxide, bicarbonate and carbonate.

METHOD B: INTERFERING SUBSTANCES (*e.g.*, VOLATILE ORGANIC COMPOUNDS, OXALATES, THIOCYANATES) KNOWN TO BE ABSENT

When volatile organic compounds, oxalates, thiocyanates, or other organic substances likely to evolve carbon dioxide or carbon monoxide on acidification, are absent, dissolved carbon dioxide and carbon present as carbonates can be removed from the acidified sample before the oxidation is begun, and the following simple procedure can be used. It is still necessary to prevent acid fumes and halogens from reaching the absorption tubes, but for this purpose an absorption tube containing a small volume of acidified potassium iodide may replace the combustion tube.

PROCEDURE—

Measure a suitable volume of sample into the flask, A, but not more than 50 ml and containing not more than 20 mg of organic carbon, and then add 150 ml of sulphuric acid. Pass a slow stream of air free from carbon dioxide through the liquid for 30 minutes. Meanwhile, measure 25 ml of barium hydroxide solution into each of the three absorption tubes and connect them in series with the absorption tube containing acidified potassium iodide, which replaces the combustion tube. Close the tubes at one end with a clip and at the other with a soda-lime guard tube.

When preparations are complete, stop the flow of air and add to the contents of the flask 10 ml of saturated chromic acid solution. Immediately connect the flask to the absorption train and open the clips. Light the micro-burner and raise the temperature until a steady stream of bubbles occurs. Do not let the gases overload the absorption train and do not heat the flask so strongly that white fumes of sulphur trioxide are evolved. Complete the determination as in Method A, starting at the paragraph beginning "Stop heating the flask and pass air free from carbon dioxide. . . ."

REFERENCE

1. Mills, E. V., *J. Soc. Chem. Ind.*, 1931, **50**, 375T.

Chloride (Chlorion)

Two methods are recommended, namely, that due to Mohr and that due to Volhard.   The latter method is included for use when the effluent contains phosphate, since this interferes in the Mohr method.

MOHR'S METHOD

PRINCIPLE OF METHOD—

The chloride, in substantially neutral solution containing chromate, is titrated with silver nitrate.   Silver chloride is precipitated and red silver chromate is formed at the end-point.

RANGE—

For chloride ion contents of 0·15 to 10 mg in the volume titrated.

APPLICABILITY—

The method is generally applicable, but ions that form insoluble salts with silver interfere.   Bromide and iodide are included as their equivalents of chloride. Sulphides, sulphites, cyanides and thiocyanates interfere, but these can be removed or destroyed by acidifying the solution with dilute nitric acid and then boiling it with hydrogen peroxide.   Alternatively, if the cyanide or thiocyanate content is known, its equivalent in terms of chloride can be deducted from the result of the titration.

Phosphate also interferes, and when this is present the chloride should be determined by Volhard's method of titration in acid solution (see below).

REAGENTS—

Aluminium hydroxide suspension—Dissolve 125 g of aluminium potassium sulphate, $Al_2(SO_4)_3.K_2SO_4.24H_2O$, in about 1 litre of distilled water.   Precipitate the aluminium hydroxide by adding ammonium hydroxide slowly in slight excess with stirring.   Allow the precipitate to settle, then wash the precipitate by decantation with distilled water until it is free from chloride.   Finally, dilute the suspension of aluminium hydroxide to 1 litre with distilled water.

*Silver nitrate solution, 0·1 N or 0·01 N.**

Potassium chromate indicator solution—Dissolve 5 g of potassium chromate in 100 ml of distilled water.   Add silver nitrate solution to produce a slight red precipitate of silver chromate and then filter the indicator solution.

PROCEDURE—

Measure a portion of the effluent sample that is expected to contain between 0·15 and 10 mg of chloride ion.   If necessary, dilute this to 100 ml.

NOTE—If the sample is coloured, decolorise the portion by adding 3 ml of aluminium hydroxide suspension.   Stir the mixture thoroughly and, after a few minutes, filter it and wash the precipitate with 10 to 15 ml of distilled water, collecting the washings.

* If it is desired to use a silver nitrate solution such that
1 ml ≡ 1 mg of chloride ion,
prepare the solution by dissolving 4·79 g of silver nitrate in distilled water and diluting to 1 litre. Standardise this solution against a sodium chloride solution containing 0·1649 g of dried sodium chloride per litre (*i.e.*, 1 ml ≡ 0·1 mg of chloride).

If necessary, add dilute sulphuric acid or dilute sodium hydroxide solution so that the liquid just decolorises phenolphthalein.   Add 1 ml of potassium chromate indicator solution and titrate with silver nitrate solution (0·1 N or 0·01 N, depending upon the expected amount of chloride) with constant stirring, until a colour change from pure yellow to pinkish yellow is perceptible.   It is easier to see the change of colour at the end-point if it is compared with an incompletely titrated sample in a similar filtration vessel.

Carry out a blank titration on 100 ml of distilled water.

Express the results as milligrams of chloride ion per litre of sample.

1 ml of 0·1 N silver nitrate solution ≡ 3·546 mg of chloride ion (Cl′).

VOLHARD'S METHOD

PRINCIPLE OF METHOD—

The chloride is titrated in acid solution with an excess of silver nitrate, the precipitated chloride is coagulated by shaking with a little nitrobenzene, and the excess of silver is titrated with thiocyanate solution, with ferric alum as indicator.

RANGE—

For amounts of chloride ion above 10 mg per litre of sample.

APPLICABILITY—

The method is generally applicable, but anions whose silver salts are insoluble in dilute nitric acid interfere.   Thiocyanate, cyanide and sulphide are destroyed as described under "Mohr's Method"; bromide and iodide are included as their equivalent of chloride.   Phosphates do not interfere.   Ferrocyanides and ferricyanides, if present in significant amounts, must be removed, e.g., by precipitation with ferric or ferrous sulphate, respectively, followed by filtration.

REAGENTS—

Nitric acid, sp.gr. 1·42.
Silver nitrate solution, 0·1 N or 0·01 N.*
Potassium thiocyanate solution, 0·1 N or 0·01 N.*
Ferric alum indicator solution—Dissolve 25 g of ferric alum in 100 ml of distilled water; clear the solution by the addition, drop by drop, of dilute sulphuric acid.
Nitrobenzene, redistilled.

PROCEDURE—

Measure a portion of the effluent sample that is expected to contain between 1 and 70 mg of chloride ion.   If necessary, dilute this to 100 ml.   Acidify with 5 ml of nitric acid.   Titrate the solution with silver nitrate solution (0·1 N or 0·01 N, depending upon the expected amount of chloride) with stirring to coagulate the precipitate.   Add about a 2-ml excess of silver nitrate solution if the 0·1 N solution is being used (or a 5-ml excess if the 0·01 N solution is used).   Add about 1 ml of nitrobenzene and stir well.   Add 1 ml of ferric alum indicator solution and titrate the excess of silver with potassium thiocyanate solution of appropriate concentration, stirring the mixture well after each addition.   The end-point is the appearance of the orange or reddish ferric thiocyanate colour.   From the burette readings and

* If it is desired to use solutions such that
1 ml of silver nitrate solution ≡ 1 mg of chloride ion,
prepare the solution of silver nitrate by the method given in the footnote to "Mohr's Method." Prepare the potassium thiocyanate solution by dissolving 2·741 g of pure potassium thiocyanate in distilled water and diluting to 1 litre.   This solution does not keep well and it should be frequently standardised by titration into a known volume of the silver nitrate solution diluted with distilled water and acidified with dilute nitric acid, with ferric alum as indicator, as in carrying out the test.

the exact concentrations of the solutions ascertain the net amount of silver nitrate used to precipitate the chloride. Express the result as milligrams of chloride ion per litre of sample.

1 ml of 0·1 N silver nitrate solution ≡ 3·546 mg of chloride ion (Cl′).

Residual Chlorine

The residual chlorine content of an effluent sample will tend to decrease after collection, particularly in hot weather and if the chlorine is not in combination with nitrogenous compounds. It is therefore important that residual chlorine tests be carried out with a minimum of delay; ideally the examination for chlorine should be made at the actual location of sampling. Provided that results of the highest accuracy are not required, commercial chlorine-testing outfits are useful for such tests made on the spot.

When the sample contains suspended matter, a portion should be allowed to stand for 15 minutes, and the supernatant liquid tested for chlorine.

In all, four methods are given, covering different ranges of chlorine content and the presence or otherwise of certain interfering compounds.

o-TOLIDINE METHOD

PRINCIPLE OF METHOD—

The colour developed by reaction of the residual chlorine with o-tolidine is compared with standards.

RANGE—

For residual chlorine contents up to 1·0 mg per litre of sample.

APPLICABILITY—

This method measures total residual chlorine (free and combined). Nitrites and ferric and manganic compounds may interfere: results are acceptable without correction if the sample contains less than 0·2 mg per litre of ferric iron or nitrite nitrogen, or less than 0·01 mg per litre of manganese in the oxidised form. When interfering oxidants are present in amounts exceeding those stated, they are separately determined after removal of the free chlorine by arsenite and the value obtained is subtracted from the uncorrected result. The interference by nitrites is more marked if the sample is unduly exposed to daylight during the test.

REAGENTS—

Hydrochloric acid, diluted (1 + 9).

o-Tolidine solution—Dissolve 1·35 g of o-tolidine hydrochloride in 1 litre of diluted hydrochloric acid (1 + 9). The solution must be stored in an amber bottle. Reagent of satisfactory quality can be purchased; if necessary, it can be prepared from less pure material by recrystallising from hot dilute hydrochloric acid solution after decolourising with activated carbon.

Sodium arsenite solution—Dissolve 0·5 g of sodium meta-arsenite, $NaAsO_2$, in distilled water and dilute to 100 ml.

Chlorine standards—Owing to the complications involved in setting up standards actually based on chlorine and to their relative instability, it has long been customary to compare the o-tolidine colours either with standard solutions containing dichromate or with coloured-glass standards. Since many laboratories are now equipped with absorptiometers, directions are also given for the preparation of the necessary "temporary" standards, which can conveniently be prepared from hypochlorite.

(a) *Permanent solution standards*—

Acid copper sulphate solution—Dissolve 1·5 g of copper sulphate, $CuSO_4.5H_2O$, in distilled water, add 1 ml of sulphuric acid, sp.gr. 1·84, and dilute to 100 ml.

Acid potassium dichromate solution—Dissolve 0·25 g of potassium dichromate in distilled water, add 1 ml of sulphuric acid, sp.gr. 1·84, and dilute to 1 litre.

Permanent standards to match the colours produced by various concentrations of chlorine are prepared according to Table IV. Mix the appropriate volumes of the acid copper sulphate and acid potassium dichromate solutions and dilute to 100 ml with distilled water.

TABLE IV

PERMANENT SOLUTION STANDARDS FOR USE IN *o*-TOLIDINE TEST
FOR RESIDUAL CHLORINE

Chlorine, mg per litre	Acid copper sulphate solution, ml	Acid potassium dichromate solution, ml	Chlorine, mg per litre	Acid copper sulphate solution, ml	Acid potassium dichromate solution, ml
0·01	0·0	0·8	0·25	1·9	25·0
0·02	0·0	2·1	0·30	1·9	30·0
0·03	0·0	3·2	0·35	1·9	34·0
0·04	0·0	4·3	0·40	2·0	38·0
0·05	0·4	5·5	0·50	2·0	45·0
0·06	0·8	6·6	0·60	2·0	51·0
0·07	1·2	7·5	0·70	2·0	58·0
0·08	1·5	8·2	0·80	2·0	63·0
0·09	1·7	9·0	0·90	2·0	67·0
0·10	1·8	10·0	1·00	2·0	72·0
0·20	1·9	20·0			

(*b*) *Coloured-glass standards*—

These are supplied with testing outfits and it is essential to follow exactly the instructions of the manufacturers for the preparation and use of the reagents.

(*c*) *Temporary chlorine standards*—

Prepare a stock solution of sodium hypochlorite to contain approximately 1 per cent. of available chlorine. Determine the strength of this solution immediately before use by delivering a known volume into an excess of 0·1 *N* sodium arsenite (containing sodium bicarbonate) and titrating the excess with 0·1 *N* iodine solution, using starch as indicator.

In the preparation of temporary chlorine standards the distilled water must be completely free from ammonia and of zero chlorine demand. To this end, ammonia-free water (prepared by distilling tap-water to which sulphuric acid and a few crystals of potassium permanganate have been added) is dosed with sufficient dilute sodium hypochlorite to give a residual chlorine reaction of about 1 mg per litre after 30 minutes. The chlorinated water (in a glass-stoppered bottle) is then allowed to stand in direct sunlight until no residual chlorine is detected when 50 ml are tested with *o*-tolidine solution. The dissipation of the excess of chlorine may take some days, even in strong sunlight.

All glassware to be used in the calibration and test should be filled with heavily chlorinated water for some hours, afterwards being rinsed thoroughly with zero-demand water.

PROCEDURE—

Should the effluent have a total alkalinity (measured as described under "Preliminary Examination of the Sample: Alkalinity") exceeding 400 mg per litre (as $CaCO_3$), add sufficient dilute hydrochloric acid to reduce the alkalinity to this figure. Carry out the test on this adjusted sample and allow for the dilution when calculating the result.

To 100 ml of the effluent sample (adjusted if necessary) add 1 ml of *o*-tolidine solution and mix rapidly. If the temperature of the sample is less than 20° C, raise it quickly to that temperature after the *o*-tolidine has been added. Allow the solution to stand in the dark for 15 minutes; then determine the chlorine content by one of the following procedures.

Express the result as milligrams of residual chlorine per litre of sample.

Use of permanent solution standards—Compare the test solutions with the standard solutions in Nessler cylinders: the colours must be viewed from above in north daylight, and not in sunlight. It must be emphasised that the amounts of copper and dichromate solutions required to match the colour produced by a given chlorine content are somewhat dependent on the depth of liquid viewed.

Permanent solution standards should only be used when the test samples are free from appreciable colour or turbidity. When they are used, results should be reported as follows—

For chlorine contents less than 0·1 mg per litre—to nearest 0·01 mg per litre.
For chlorine contents between 0·1 and 0·4 mg per litre—to nearest 0·05 mg per litre.
For chlorine contents more than 0·4 mg per litre—to nearest 0·1 mg per litre.

Use of coloured-glass standards—Proprietary testing outfits should only be used in accordance with the makers' instructions, and the analyst must make sure that the results so obtained agree with those given by either of the two other procedures. Testing outfits are useful for field work, and are especially valuable because they readily permit compensation for colour and turbidity by placing behind the standard glass a control tube containing a portion of the sample that has not been treated with the *o*-tolidine solution. It is recommended, however, that this control tube should contain a portion of the sample that has been acidified (1 ml of diluted hydrochloric acid (1 + 9) per 100 ml) in case acid-soluble suspended matter is present.

Instrumental method—Measure the optical density of the test solution in a spectrophotometer or in an absorptiometer, using a 1-cm cell and a wavelength of 4350 A in a spectrophotometer or a suitable violet filter in an absorptiometer. Use distilled water in the comparison cell. Read the number of milligrams of chlorine equivalent to the observed optical density from a previously prepared calibration graph and, after allowing for any initial dilution of the sample, obtain the net measure of residual chlorine in it.

Establish the calibration graph as follows—

From the stock hypochlorite solution, prepare a series of standards covering the range 0·02 to 1·0 mg of available chlorine per litre, using zero-demand water at a temperature of 20° to 22° C for the dilutions. Do not prepare more than two or three of these diluted solutions at a time, and add the *o*-tolidine reagent (as described for the test solution) immediately afterwards. Allow the solutions to stand for 15 minutes in the dark and measure the optical densities, using 1-cm cells and using distilled water in the comparison cell. Construct a graph relating the optical densities to the number of milligrams of chlorine per litre.

To correct for colour or turbidity, measure also the optical density of the sample after addition of 1 ml of diluted hydrochloric acid (1 + 9), using the same cell-length and wavelength or filter as before. Subtract the value obtained from the gross optical density previously measured in the presence of *o*-tolidine; the difference then corresponds to the true residual chlorine content.

Samples containing oxidising agents—To 100 ml of the sample add 2 ml of sodium arsenite solution, mix and at once add 1 ml of *o*-tolidine solution. Mix again and raise the temperature to 20° C if necessary. Allow the solution to stand in the dark for 15 minutes: any colour that develops will be due to interfering oxidants. Measure it in terms of residual chlorine content and subtract the value obtained from the gross value for residual chlorine to give the true chlorine content.

IODIMETRIC METHOD

PRINCIPLE OF METHOD—

Iodine is liberated from potassium iodide by the chlorine and is titrated with sodium thiosulphate solution.

RANGE—

The method is suitable for residual chlorine contents in the range 1 to 10 mg per litre of sample. Higher concentrations can be determined by suitably adjusting the volume of the sample and, if necessary, the concentrations and amounts of the reagents.

APPLICABILITY—

Nitrites and ferric and manganic compounds interfere with the method, which involves titration in dilute acetic acid. When these substances are present, the titre obtained within the pH range 4·5 to 8·0 will usually approximate to the true chlorine equivalent.

It must be stated whether or not the titration was made in acid solution.

REAGENTS—

Potassium iodide solution, 10 *per cent. w/v.*

Acetic acid, glacial.

Potassium iodate solution, 0·005 N—This solution may conveniently be prepared by diluting a stronger standard solution (*e.g.,* the $N/80$ solution used in the Permanganate Value test (see "Oxygen Demand"), 100 ml diluted to 250 ml).

Sodium thiosulphate solution, A (*approximately* 0·25 N)—Dissolve 63 g of sodium thiosulphate, $Na_2S_2O_3.5H_2O$, in 1 litre of boiled and cooled distilled water.

Sodium thiosulphate solution, B (*approximately* 0·005 N)—Dilute 20·0 ml of solution A to 1 litre. This solution must be standardised immediately before use with standard potassium iodate solution, as follows—

Cool 500 ml of distilled water to below 20° C, add 10·0 ml of 0·005 N potassium iodate solution, and then 5 ml of potassium iodide solution and 5 ml of acetic acid. Mix and allow the solution to stand for 1 minute. Titrate with sodium thiosulphate solution B, with constant swirling, until the colour of the liberated iodine is nearly discharged; then add 2 ml of starch indicator solution and continue the titration until the blue colour disappears for at least 30 seconds.

Starch indicator solution.

PROCEDURE—

Not more than 2 mg of ferric iron per litre should be present; nitrites and oxidised manganese must be absent.

Should the effluent have a total alkalinity (measured as described under "Preliminary Examination of the Sample: Alkalinity") exceeding 400 mg per litre (as $CaCO_3$), add sufficient dilute hydrochloric acid to reduce the alkalinity to this figure. Carry out the test on this adjusted sample and allow for the dilution when calculating the result.

Cool 500 ml of the sample (adjusted if necessary) to below 20° C, add 5 ml of potassium iodide solution (or 0·5 g of solid potassium iodide) and 5 ml of acetic acid. Mix and at once titrate with sodium thiosulphate solution B until the colour of the liberated iodine is nearly discharged; then add 2 ml of starch indicator solution and continue the titration until the blue colour disappears for at least 30 seconds.

1 ml of 0·005 N thiosulphate $\equiv$ 0·1773 mg of chlorine.

Express the result as milligrams of residual chlorine per litre of sample.

Modification when nitrite, oxidised manganese or more than 2 mg of ferric iron per litre are present—Adjust the pH of the sample to between 4·5 and 8·0 by addition of acetic acid (or sodium acetate) as necessary. Titrate the solution as described above, but omit the addition of any further acetic acid.

NOTE—If there were transient existence of dichloramine in an effluent, the neutral titration might give low results: such a circumstance would, however, seldom occur.

Cyanides and Thiocyanate

Three methods are given.

In the *titration method*,[1] which is applicable to the higher concentrations of cyanide, a preliminary distillation with acid cuprous chloride is used for the determination of *total* cyanide: any complex cyanides that produce hydrogen cyanide under these conditions will be included. However, by the use of lead acetate instead of acid cuprous chloride, ferrocyanide (which is relatively non-toxic) is excluded and can be separately determined in the residue after distillation.

Aldridge's method,[2] which is applicable to low concentrations of cyanide, is used for the determination of any compounds that produce thiocyanate or cyanide radicles under the conditions of the test: ferrocyanide, ferricyanide and cyanate are not determined. A modification is given for the separate determination of thiocyanate.

In the *ferric thiocyanate method*, thiocyanate *alone* is determined.

Any determination of cyanide should be made as soon as possible after the sample has been collected, since many cyanides are relatively unstable. If delay in the analysis is unavoidable, the pH of the sample should be raised to 11 or above by the addition of sodium hydroxide, and the sample subsequently stored in a cool place.

TITRATION METHOD

PRINCIPLE OF METHOD—

After distillation of hydrogen cyanide, the cyanide is titrated directly with silver nitrate, using *p*-dimethylaminobenzylidine rhodanine as indicator.

RANGE—

For cyanide contents (as CN′) above 10 mg per litre of sample.

APPARATUS—

An all-glass distillation apparatus, fitted with a splash-head and a vertical water-cooled condenser.

REAGENTS—

Sodium hydroxide solution, approximately 2·5 N.

Silver nitrate solution, 0·1 N *or* 0·01 N.

For use in methods (*a*) and (*c*)—

Acid cuprous chloride solution—A 2 per cent. w/v solution in approximately 5 N hydrochloric acid. Prepare this solution freshly as required.

Rhodanine indicator solution—A 0·02 per cent. w/v solution of *p*-dimethylaminobenzylidine rhodanine in acetone.

For use in method (*b*)—

Lead acetate solution—Dissolve 200 g of lead acetate, $(CH_3COO)_2Pb.3H_2O$, in 1 litre of distilled water.

Methyl orange indicator solution—A 0·04 per cent. w/v aqueous solution.

PROCEDURE—

(a) Determination of total cyanide, including ferrocyanide

Measure into the distillation flask a suitable volume of the effluent sample (containing 10 to 15 mg of cyanide ion when the content is less than 200 mg per litre, or containing at least 100 mg of cyanide ion when the content is greater than 200 mg per litre), and adjust the volume to about 400 ml with distilled water. Add 10 ml of acid cuprous chloride solution and assemble the apparatus.

Place a conical flask containing 10 ml of sodium hydroxide solution under the condenser, so that the end dips below the surface. Distil the mixture and, when 50 ml of distillate have been collected in the flask, replace it by a second flask containing 10 ml of sodium hydroxide solution and collect a further 50 ml. If necessary, continue the distillation into a succession of flasks until all the hydrogen cyanide has been distilled.

Titrate the contents of the flasks separately with 0·01 N silver nitrate solution (or 0·1 N silver nitrate solution if the cyanide content of the sample is greater than 200 mg per litre), using 2 drops of rhodanine indicator solution in each flask (see Note). The end-point is indicated by the appearance of a red colour. Calculate the cyanide content from the sum of the titrations.

1 ml of 0·01 N silver nitrate solution ≡ 0·52 mg of cyanide ion.

Express the result as milligrams of total cyanide (as CN′) per litre of sample.

NOTE—It is important to use the minimum amount of indicator: an excess masks the end-point of the titration.

(b) Determination of cyanide, excluding ferrocyanide

Measure into the distillation flask a suitable volume of the effluent sample (containing not more than 200 mg of cyanide in any form) and add mineral acid or sodium hydroxide as necessary to make the solution approximately neutral to methyl orange. Dilute the solution to 400 ml and add 10 ml of lead acetate solution. Proceed to determine the cyanide as in method (a), commencing at "Place a conical flask . . ." in the second paragraph.

NOTE—Nickel and copper complex cyanides distil only slowly under the conditions of the test, and distillation may have to be prolonged.

(c) Determination of ferrocyanide

The residue in the distillation flask after the determination of cyanide in method (b) can be used for the determination of ferrocyanide. Dilute the mixture to 400 ml with distilled water and add 10 ml of acid cuprous chloride solution. Proceed to determine the cyanide as in method (a), commencing at "Place a conical flask . . ." in the second paragraph.

ALDRIDGE'S METHOD

PRINCIPLE OF METHOD—

In this method, cyanide and thiocyanate are converted to cyanogen bromide, which is then determined colorimetrically as the red compound formed by coupling with benzidine in pyridine solution.

RANGE—

For cyanide contents (as CN′) up to 2 mg per litre of sample (or up to 20 mg per litre, after dilution).

APPLICABILITY—

The method is generally applicable for the determination of any compound that produces –CN or –CNS radicles on acidification. Ferrocyanide, ferricyanide and cyanate are *not* determined.

REAGENTS—

Bromine water, saturated.

Arsenious acid solution—Dissolve 2 g of arsenious oxide, As_2O_3, in 100 ml of distilled water.

Benzidine reagent—Dissolve 5 g of benzidine hydrochloride in 100 ml of distilled water containing 2 ml of hydrochloric acid, sp.gr. 1·18. Prepare this solution freshly as required.

Pyridine solution—An approximately 60 per cent. v/v solution in distilled water (the mixture of constant boiling-point).

Acetic acid, approximately 2 N.

Standard cyanide solution—Dissolve 1·25 g of potassium cyanide in 500 ml of distilled water. Standardise this solution frequently with 0·01 N silver nitrate solution (1 ml ≡ 0·52 mg of CN'), using rhodanine indicator solution (see "Titration Method"). Adjust the solution so that 1 ml contains 1 mg of CN'.

From this stock solution prepare a dilute solution freshly as required by diluting 10·0 ml to 1 litre with distilled water, and diluting this a further 10 times.

$$1 \text{ ml} \equiv 1 \text{ } \mu g \text{ of cyanide (CN')}.$$

PROCEDURE—

(a) Determination of cyanide and thiocyanate

Into a glass-stoppered tube (calibrated at 10 ml) measure 2 ml of the effluent sample, adjusted by dilution if necessary to contain not more than 2 μg of cyanide ion. Acidify with acetic acid; then add 0·2 ml of bromine water and mix thoroughly. Add 0·2 ml of arsenious acid to remove excess of bromine; remove any bromine vapour by blowing across the mouth of the tube. Mix 3 ml of pyridine solution with 0·6 ml of benzidine reagent, add this mixture to the contents of the tube, dilute to the mark with distilled water and mix thoroughly. Stopper the tube and allow the mixture to stand in the dark for 25 to 30 minutes at a temperature between 15° and 20° C.

Carry out a blank procedure on all the reagents used.

Proceed to determine the cyanide content (including thiocyanate) colorimetrically, either instrumentally or by visual colour comparison.

Express the result in terms of cyanide (as CN') as milligrams per litre of sample.

Instrumental method—Measure the optical densities of the test and blank solutions in a spectrophotometer or in an absorptiometer, using 1-cm cells, and using a wavelength of 5200 A in a spectrophotometer or a suitable green filter in an absorptiometer. Use distilled water in the comparison cell. Read the number of micrograms of cyanide ion equivalent to the observed optical densities of the test and blank solutions from a previously prepared calibration graph, and so obtain the net measure of cyanide ion in the sample.

Establish the calibration graph as follows—

Into a series of stoppered tubes measure appropriate amounts of standard cyanide solution, covering the range 0 to 2 μg of cyanide ion, and proceed as for the test solution. Measure the optical densities and construct a graph relating the optical densities to the number of micrograms of cyanide ion.

Visual colour-comparison method—Compare the colour of the test and standard solutions directly in the tubes.

Alternatively, proprietary coloured discs may be used in a comparator instead of the standard solutions, and the makers' instructions should be followed. The analyst must make sure that the results so obtained agree with those given by the recommended method.

(b) Separate determinations of cyanide and thiocyanate

In another tube, acidify a second similar volume of effluent sample with acetic acid. Bubble a stream of air through the solution for about 15 minutes to remove hydrogen cyanide. Add 0·2 ml of bromine water and mix thoroughly; then proceed to determine the cyanide as in method (a) above, commencing at "Add 0·2 ml of arsenious acid. . . ."

This gives the amount of cyanide equivalent to the amount of thiocyanate originally present.

The difference between the two results gives the cyanide originally present as such in the sample.

FERRIC THIOCYANATE METHOD

PRINCIPLE OF METHOD—

The red colour of ferric thiocyanate, produced by the direct addition of a ferric salt, is compared visually with standards.

RANGE—

For thiocyanate contents above 1 mg per litre of sample.

APPLICABILITY—

The method is generally applicable, but mercuric salts and oxalic acid interfere. It is useful as a rapid method of determination, but it is not a method of the highest accuracy since the colour fades in sunlight and its intensity depends on the amount of ferric salt added and on the presence of sulphate.

To compensate for any colour in the sample itself, use is made of mercuric chloride.[3]

REAGENTS—

Hydrochloric acid, approximately 0·1 N.

Ferric chloride solution—Dissolve 10 g of ferric chloride, $FeCl_3.6H_2O$, in 1 litre of distilled water.

Mercuric chloride solution, saturated.

Standard thiocyanate solution—Dissolve about 5 g of potassium thiocyanate in distilled water and dilute to 500 ml. Determine the thiocyanate content by titration with 0·1 N silver nitrate solution, using Volhard's method (1 ml of 0·1 N $AgNO_3$ ≡ 5·81 mg of CNS'). Adjust the solution so that 1 ml contains 5·0 mg of CNS'.

Dilute 10·0 ml of this solution to 500 ml with distilled water freshly as required.

$$1 \text{ ml} \equiv 0\cdot1 \text{ mg of CNS}'.$$

PROCEDURE—

To 50 ml of the filtered effluent sample (or an aliquot diluted to 50 ml) in a Nessler cylinder add 0·5 ml of 0·1 N hydrochloric acid and 0·5 ml of ferric chloride solution. To a second cylinder containing rather less than 50 ml of distilled water also add 0·5 ml of hydrochloric acid and 0·5 ml of ferric chloride solution. From a burette add, drop by drop, standard thiocyanate solution to the second cylinder, stirring after each addition, until the colour matches that in the first cylinder. Note the volume of standard thiocyanate used (*x* ml).

To the first cylinder containing the sample add 1 ml of mercuric chloride solution to discharge the red thiocyanate colour. Compare any residual colour with standard thiocyanate as described above, and note the volume used (y ml).

$$\text{Thiocyanate in sample (mg of CNS' per litre)} = \frac{100\,(x-y)}{\text{ml of sample}}$$

NOTE—Great care must be taken to avoid accidental contamination of the contents of the cylinders with mercuric chloride.

REFERENCES

1. Williams, H. E., "Cyanogen Compounds; their Chemistry, Detection and Estimation," Second Edition, Edward Arnold and Co., London, 1948, pp. 168 and 366.
2. Aldridge, W. N., *Analyst*, 1944, **69**, 262; 1945, **70**, 474.
3. Ministry of Housing and Local Government, "Methods of Chemical Analysis as applied to Sewage and Sewage Effluents," Second Edition, H.M. Stationery Office, 1956, p. 74.

Synthetic Detergents

After considering the available methods of determination, the Ministry of Housing and Local Government Committee on Synthetic Detergents only recommended a method for the anionic type, namely, that of Longwell and Maniece.[1] The A.B.C.M. - S.A.C. Joint Committee, however, considered that it would be helpful to describe methods for the non-ionic and cationic types, since these are used in industry, although they comprise only about 5 per cent. of the total domestic and industrial usage. Apart from the Longwell and Maniece method, the remaining methods have therefore been included *for information* and it must be emphasised that they should be regarded as tentative only.

The methods of Epton[2] and of Barr, Oliver and Stubbings[3] were originally devised for the determination of anionic surface-active agents present in fairly high concentration in synthetic-detergent preparations. By a reversal of the technique of Epton's method (Method A) it is possible to determine cation-active materials. Apart from results by the method of Longwell and Maniece, any estimate of surface-active compounds (in low concentration) is open to doubt when suspended solids are present.

ANIONIC DETERGENTS
(LOW CONCENTRATIONS)

PRINCIPLE OF METHOD—

In this method, due to Longwell and Maniece,[1] a complex of the detergent with methylene blue in alkaline solution is extracted with chloroform. After the chloroform extract has been washed with an acid solution of methylene blue, it is compared colorimetrically with standards prepared from Manoxol O.T.

RANGE—

For contents of anion-active material from 20 to 150 μg.

REAGENTS—

Alkaline phosphate solution—Dissolve 10 g of analytical-reagent grade anhydrous disodium hydrogen phosphate in distilled water. Adjust the pH to 10 by adding sodium hydroxide solution and dilute to 1 litre with distilled water.

Neutral methylene blue solution—Dissolve 0·35 g of methylene blue, B.P., in distilled water and dilute to 1 litre.

Acid methylene blue solution—Dissolve 0·35 g of methylene blue, B.P., in about 500 ml of distilled water, add 6·5 ml of sulphuric acid, sp.gr. 1·84, and dilute to 1 litre with distilled water.

Chloroform—Analytical-reagent grade.

Standard solution of anion-active agent—Dissolve 0·100 g of Manoxol O.T. (sodium dioctylsulphosuccinate) in distilled water and dilute to 1 litre.

Dilute 10 ml of this solution to 100 ml with distilled water. Prepare this solution freshly as required.

$$1 \text{ ml} \equiv 10 \ \mu g \text{ of Manoxol O.T.}$$

PROCEDURE—

(*i*) Measure into a separating funnel a volume of sample preferably containing between 20 and 150 μg of anion-active material. (It is generally impracticable to take more than 10 ml of crude or settled sewage, owing to emulsification on shaking with chloroform, but it is possible to take up to 100 ml of good-quality effluent when the detergent content is very low.) If sulphide is present, proceed as described in Note 1. Dilute the contents of the funnel to 100 ml with distilled water. Add 10 ml of alkaline phosphate solution, 5 ml of neutral methylene blue solution and 15 ml of chloroform.

(*ii*) Shake the mixture evenly and gently twice a second for 1 minute. Allow the layers to separate, breaking up any emulsion formed in the funnel by gentle agitation with the flattened end of a glass rod. Run the clear chloroform layer into a second separating funnel containing 100 ml of distilled water and 5 ml of acid methylene blue solution. Rinse the first funnel with 2 ml of chloroform added from a burette and then run this rinsing into the second funnel.

(*iii*) Shake the contents of the second funnel as before and allow the layers to separate. Run the chloroform layer through a small filter-funnel plugged with cotton-wool moistened with chloroform into a 50-ml calibrated flask, rinsing with a further 2 ml of chloroform.

(*iv*) Repeat operations (*ii*) and (*iii*), using two 10-ml portions of chloroform. Dilute the combined extracts in the flask to the mark with chloroform. (See Note 2.)

Measure the optical densities of the chloroform extract and of the blank in a spectrophotometer or in an absorptiometer, using a wavelength of 6500 A in a spectrophotometer, or a suitable orange filter if an absorptiometer is used. Read the number of micrograms of detergent, in terms of anion-active material, equivalent to the observed optical densities of the test and blank solutions from a previously prepared calibration graph, and so obtain the net measure of detergent in the sample.

Express the anion-active content of the sample as milligrams per litre in terms of Manoxol O.T.

Establish the calibration graph as follows—

Treat appropriate amounts of dilute Manoxol O.T. solution covering the range 20 to 200 μg as for the test solution and determine the optical densities. Construct a graph relating the optical density to the concentration.

NOTES—1. *Sulphide interference*—Sulphide, if present, must be oxidised before extraction. Place the required volume of sample in the first separating funnel, and add 10 ml of alkaline phosphate solution and 2 ml of 20-volume hydrogen peroxide. Allow the mixture to stand for 5 minutes and then dilute it to 110 ml with distilled water. Add 5 ml of neutral methylene blue solution and 15 ml of chloroform, and continue as from paragraph (*ii*) of the procedure.

2. Before a further determination is carried out, the separating funnels should be rinsed with dilute nitric acid to remove adsorbed methylene blue.

ANIONIC DETERGENTS
(HIGH CONCENTRATIONS)

Two methods are described.

Method A[2] has some advantage with slightly opalescent samples. Reversal of the technique of this method may be used for estimating cation-active materials (see p. 94).

Method B[3] is applicable to clear solutions and has a direct end-point.

METHOD A

PRINCIPLE OF METHOD—

This method utilises the fact that cation-active materials decompose the chloroform-soluble complex formed between anion-active materials and methylene blue, water-soluble methylene blue being liberated.

RANGE—

For contents of anion-active agents above 10 mg per litre of sample.

REAGENTS—

Chloroform B.P.

Methylene blue solution—Dissolve 0·003 g of methylene blue, B.P., and 5 g of anhydrous sodium sulphate in 100 ml of distilled water containing 1·2 per cent. of sulphuric acid, sp.gr. 1·84.

Standard solution of anion-active agent (Manoxol O.T.)—Dissolve 2·22 g of Manoxol O.T. in 1 litre of distilled water.

Solution of cation-active agent (cetylpyridinium bromide)—Dissolve 1·54 g of cetylpyridinium bromide in 1 litre of distilled water.

PROCEDURE—

Standardisation of cetylpyridinium bromide solution—Transfer by pipette 10·0 ml of the standard solution of Manoxol O.T. to a 250-ml glass-stoppered flask. Add 25 ml of methylene blue solution and 15 ml of chloroform. Shake the flask with just sufficient force to ensure that the phases mix thoroughly. At this stage the upper layer is pale blue and the lower layer is dark blue. From a burette add cetylpyridinium bromide solution 2 ml at a time with intermittent shaking. When the colour of the upper layer begins to deepen, reduce the rate of addition. The end-point is reached when both layers are the same colour when viewed in reflected light.

Titration of sample—In a similar manner, titrate a suitable aliquot of the effluent sample with the standardised cetylpyridinium bromide solution. The volume of sample taken should preferably contain approximately the equivalent of 0·02 g of Manoxol O.T. (or approximately 0·005 M with respect to its anion-active agent content).

Express the anion-active agent content of the sample as milligrams per litre in terms of Manoxol O.T.

METHOD B

PRINCIPLE OF METHOD—

In this method the anion-active material in the sample is titrated with standard cation-active material. The end-point is marked by the appearance of a blue colour due to the formation of a complex between the excess cation-active material and bromophenol blue, this complex being soluble in chloroform.

RANGE—

For contents of anion-active agent above 10 mg per litre of sample.

REAGENTS—

Chloroform, B.P.

Bromophenol blue indicator solution—A 0·04 per cent. solution in 20 per cent. aqueous ethanol.

Standard solution of anion-active agent (Manoxol O.T.)—Dissolve 0·444 g of Manoxol O.T. in 1 litre of distilled water.

Solution of cation-active agent (cetyltrimethylammonium bromide)—Dissolve 0·364 g of cetyltrimethylammonium bromide in 1 litre of distilled water.

PROCEDURE—

Standardisation of cetyltrimethylammonium bromide solution—Transfer by pipette 25·0 ml of the standard solution of Manoxol O.T. to a glass-stoppered flask and add 100 ml of distilled water, 50 ml of chloroform and 5 drops of bromophenol blue indicator solution. Titrate the mixture with cetyltrimethylammonium bromide solution, shaking after each addition. In the early stages of the titration, the chloroform emulsifies in the aqueous phase, but ready separation into two layers occurs as the titration proceeds, particularly as the end-point is approached. Allow about 1 minute to elapse between successive additions, in 0·1-ml increments towards the end-point, which is taken as the point at which the first indication of blue colour appears in the chloroform layer. The blue colour intensifies with further additions of cetyltrimethylammonium bromide solution.

Titration of sample—In a similar manner, titrate a suitable aliquot of the effluent sample with the standardised cetyltrimethylammonium bromide solution. The volume of sample taken should contain approximately the equivalent of 0·01 g of Manoxol O.T.

Express the anion-active agent content of the sample as milligrams per litre in terms of Manoxol O.T.

CATIONIC DETERGENTS
(CONCENTRATIONS GREATER THAN 10 mg PER LITRE)

As mentioned in the introductory paragraphs, a reversal of the technique described under Anionic Detergents, Method A, may be used to estimate cation-active materials.

REAGENTS—

As for Anionic Detergents, Method A, but with the cetylpyridinium bromide as the standard.

PROCEDURE—

Standardisation of Manoxol O.T. solution—Transfer by pipette to a 250-ml glass-stoppered flask 10·0 ml of standard cetylpyridinium bromide solution. Add 25 ml of methylene blue solution and 15 ml of chloroform. Shake the flask with just sufficient force to ensure thorough mixing of the two phases. At this stage the upper layer is dark blue and the lower layer is pale blue.

From a burette add the solution of Manoxol O.T., 1 ml at a time with intermittent shaking, allowing 1 minute to elapse between successive additions. When the colour of the lower layer begins to deepen, reduce the rate of addition. The end-point is reached when both layers are the same colour when viewed in reflected light.

Titration of sample—In a similar manner, titrate a suitable aliquot of the effluent sample with the standardised solution of Manoxol O.T. The volume of sample taken should preferably contain approximately the equivalent of 0·015 g of cetylpyridinium bromide. From the standard titration and the sample calculate the number of milligrams of cation-active material present and express the result in terms of milligrams of cetylpyridinium bromide per litre of sample.

CATIONIC DETERGENTS
(Concentrations less than 10 mg per litre)

A method of direct estimation cannot, as yet, be recommended. However, a method depending upon the reduction of anionic activity has given reasonable results.[4] It is offered here tentatively.

PRINCIPLE OF METHOD—

When anion-active and cation-active materials are mixed, in solution, mutual neutralisation of the activities takes place. However, the decrease in apparent anionic activity is not exactly proportional to the amount of cationic detergent present, but falls off as the amount of cationic material is increased in the presence of a constant amount of anionic material.

PROCEDURE—

First obtain an approximation (in mg per litre) of the concentration of cation-active material in the effluent sample, as follows—

Shake various aliquots of the sample with an aqueous solution of anion-active material of known concentration (about 15 mg per litre). Treat these mixtures, and the pure solution of the anion-active material, according to Degens's single acid-extraction method for anion-active material[5]: in this method (see below), the free anion-active material forms with methylene blue a coloured complex, which is extracted by chloroform. The approximate concentration of cation-active material in the sample is then assessed by selecting, by means of simple visual inspection of the chloroform extracts, that aliquot of sample showing a reduction by half or more of the colour produced by the solution of anion-active material alone.

Proceed to estimate more closely the concentration of cation-active material present. Into a series of separating funnels measure, respectively, 10-ml portions of solutions containing amounts of standard cation-active material around the approximate value of the sample in steps of -2, -1, $+1$ and $+2$ mg per litre. Into another separating funnel measure the previously ascertained volume of the effluent sample. Shake the contents of each funnel with 10 ml of a solution of standard anion-active material having a known concentration of about 15 mg per litre. Proceed to estimate, in each case, the uncombined anion-active material by Degens's method. The reduction in anionic activity effected by the sample can then be related to that effected by the standard cation-active material, and so assessed. Express the content of cation-active material as milligrams per litre of sample.

NOTE—Certain ions, *e.g.*, nitrate and chloride, interfere with Degens's method. If these are present, they should be present in the standard in the same concentration as in the sample.

Degens's method—In a small separating funnel put 10 ml of chloroform, 100 ml of distilled water, 10 ml of the anion-active test solution and 5 ml of acid methylene blue solution (see under "Reagents," Anionic Detergents, Longwell and Maniece method). Shake the mixture for 1 minute, at the rate of 2 shakes per second. Extract three times with 10-ml portions of chloroform, filtering each chloroform extract through the same plug of cotton-wool into a 50-ml calibrated flask, and dilute the solution to the mark with chloroform. Measure the optical density by any suitable instrument that has been calibrated in terms of standard anion-active material, *e.g.*, Manoxol O.T., treated as above.

NON-IONIC DETERGENTS
(Tentative method)

The method[6],[7] described below may be found useful for the determination in trade effluents of non-ionic polyoxyethylene-type detergents (*e.g.*, Lissapol N) when the concentration is greater than 10 mg per litre of sample; at concentrations below this the method is not reliable, and even at the higher concentrations it should be accepted with some reserve, particularly when the protein content is high.

Principle of method—

The non-ionic detergent is determined by precipitation of a detergent - barium molybdophosphate complex from an aqueous ethanolic solution of the ether extract of the sample. The precipitate is either (*i*) dissolved in ethylene glycol monomethyl ether (methyl Cellosolve) and hydrochloric acid, and its optical density determined in an ultra-violet spectrophotometer at a wavelength of 3100 A, or (*ii*) digested with a mixture of sulphuric and perchloric acids, and the phosphate determined colorimetrically.

> Note—This method can be applied direct to good-quality effluents, but, for those with a high protein content, a preliminary deproteinisation with zinc sulphate and barium hydroxide is usually necessary. However, deproteinisation leads to appreciable loss of non-ionic detergent, presumably owing to adsorption by the precipitate. This can be allowed for by applying a correction factor of 1·4, but results obtained on such deproteinised samples must be regarded as approximate.

Owing to the very small amounts of solids precipitated, their separation from liquids is effected by spinning in a centrifuge and all operations subsequent to the extraction with ether and before the colour measurement are carried out in one and the same centrifuge tube.

Range—

For non-ionic detergent (active agent) contents above 10 mg per litre of sample.

Reagents—

Barium chloride solution—Dissolve 10 g of barium chloride, $BaCl_2.2H_2O$, in 90 ml of distilled water.

Molybdophosphoric acid solution, 1 per cent. w/v.

Zinc sulphate solution—Dissolve 5 g of zinc sulphate, $ZnSO_4.7H_2O$, in distilled water and dilute to 100 ml.

Barium hydroxide solution—To 4·75 g of barium hydroxide, $Ba(OH)_2.8H_2O$, add 100 ml of distilled water and boil gently, with stirring, for 2 minutes. Filter hot through filter-paper into a bottle; keep the bottle well stoppered to minimise the formation of barium carbonate.

Hydrochloric acid, diluted (1 + 1)—Mix equal volumes of hydrochloric acid, sp.gr. 1·18, and distilled water.

Hydrochloric acid, dilute (1 + 9).

Acid ethylene glycol monomethyl ether—To 400 ml of the freshly distilled reagent add 100 ml of diluted hydrochloric acid (1 + 1), mix well and cool.

Acid ammonium molybdate solution—Dissolve 10 g of ammonium molybdate, $(NH_4)_6Mo_7O_{24}.4H_2O$, in 100 ml of distilled water, pour the solution into a well cooled mixture of 150 ml of sulphuric acid, sp.gr. 1·84, and 150 ml of distilled water, and mix well. Protect the solution from light.

Metol - sulphite solution (Tschopps's reagent)—Dissolve 40 g of sodium meta-bisulphite and 1 g of sodium sulphite, $Na_2SO_3.7H_2O$, in cold distilled water, add

0·2 g of Metol (*p*-methylaminophenol sulphate) and stir well until dissolved. Dilute the solution to 100 ml and mix well.

Perchloric acid, 60 *per cent. w/v.*

Sulphuric acid, diluted (1 + 1)—Carefully add 1 volume of sulphuric acid, sp.gr. 1·84, to 1 volume of distilled water, stirring during the addition.

Sodium chloride.

Diethyl ether.

Aqueous ethanol, 20 *per cent. v/v.*

Sodium hydroxide solution, N.

Lissapol N active agent*—For preparation of standard solutions.

PROCEDURE—

Clear effluents—

Weigh 15 g of sodium chloride into a dry 100-ml separating funnel with a short stem. Pour into the funnel 40·0 ml of the sample. Add 10 ml of distilled water and 10 ml of ether measured with a graduated cylinder, place the stopper in the funnel and shake vigorously until the sodium chloride has almost completely dissolved. Allow the mixture to stand for at least 5 minutes. Run the aqueous layer into a 100-ml beaker. Swirl the ether layer gently in the funnel and allow to stand for another minute. Run off the extra 0·5 ml or so of aqueous layer into the beaker containing the rest of the aqueous layer. Into the neck of the funnel insert a rubber bung carrying two narrow glass tubes, the first of which reaches just inside the rubber bung and is bent at an angle of about 60° to the vertical outside the funnel, and the second of which reaches right to the bottom of the funnel and is bent at an angle of 120° to the vertical outside the funnel. This second tube is drawn out to a fairly coarse jet at each end. By blowing into the first tube, expel about 3 to 4 ml of the ether extract into a 15-ml graduated centrifuge tube, which contains a small piece of porous pot and which is immersed for about half its length in water in a 250-ml beaker. Warm the beaker on the top of a steam-bath until the ether boils *gently*. When all the ether has evaporated, blow in another 3 to 4 ml and repeat the evaporation in stages until all the ether has been removed from the funnel. Return the separated aqueous layer from the 100-ml beaker to the funnel and extract again with 10 ml of ether, separating and evaporating the ether extract as before.

Wash down the sides of the tube with 3 ml of aqueous ethanol. Warm the tube in boiling water until the contents begin to boil. Remove from the water bath and add successively 1 ml of diluted hydrochloric acid (1 + 1), 0·5 ml of barium chloride solution and 2 ml of molybdophosphoric acid solution. Stir the contents of the tube with a glass rod until homogeneous and wash down the rod with 1 or 2 ml of dilute hydrochloric acid (1 + 9), allowing the washings to run into the tube. Remove the tube from the bath and allow it to stand for at least 2 hours, preferably overnight.

Dilute to the 10-ml mark with dilute hydrochloric acid (1 + 9) and spin in a centrifuge for 5 minutes at about 1500 r.p.m. and 20-cm radius. Using a "wash-bottle" fitting similar to that used in transferring ether from the funnel to the tube, remove the supernatant liquid. For this operation, lower the end of the long tube until it is level with the 0·4-ml mark in the centrifuge tube. Collect the expelled liquid in another centrifuge tube and examine it carefully for suspended matter. If any is present, indicating disturbance of the precipitate, return the liquor to the precipitation tube, again spin in a centrifuge and remove in a similar manner the liquor into the second tube. Pour about 2 ml of dilute hydrochloric acid (1 + 9) into the tube and disperse the precipitate thoroughly by stirring with a thin glass rod. Wash down the rod into the tube with 1 or 2 ml of dilute hydrochloric acid (1 + 9) and

* Subsequently referred to as Lissapol NX.

then fill the tube to the 10-ml mark with dilute hydrochloric acid (1 + 9).   Spin in a centrifuge and remove the supernatant liquid as before.

Determine the amount of Lissapol NX in the precipitate indirectly by measuring its molybdophosphoric acid content in either of the following ways.

Ultra-violet spectrophotometric method—Pour into the centrifuge tube containing the precipitate about 4 to 5 ml of acid ethylene glycol monomethyl ether.   Disperse the precipitate with a thin glass rod and stir the contents of the tube until solution is complete or nearly so.   Wash down the rod into the tube with 1 or 2 ml of the reagent and fill the tube to about the 9-ml mark.   Pour its contents into a 25-ml calibrated flask and wash out with further 10-ml and 5-ml portions of the reagent, adding the washings to the flask.   Dilute to the mark with acid ethylene glycol monomethyl ether and mix well.

Measure the optical density of the solution in a 1-cm cell at 3100 A, using a spectrophotometer with the acid ethylene glycol monomethyl ether reagent as reference liquid.   From a calibration graph (see later) read the concentration of active agent (in milligrams per litre), in terms of Lissapol NX, corresponding to the observed optical density.

Colorimetric molybdenum blue method (*see Note* 1)—To the centrifuge tube containing the washed precipitate add 1·0 ml of diluted sulphuric acid (1 + 1) in such a way as to wash down the sides of the tube; then add 0·2 ml of perchloric acid and 0·5 ml of *N* sodium hydroxide solution.   Warm the contents of the tube for a few seconds on a steam-bath and pour the mixture into a 25-ml beaker.   Wash the tube with several small amounts of hot distilled water, adding the washings to the beaker.   Evaporate the contents of the beaker until fumes appear.   Allow the contents to cool, add 7 ml of distilled water and heat on a steam-bath for 10 to 15 minutes.   Filter the solution through a 9-cm Whatman No. 42 filter-paper into a 8-inch × 1¼-inch boiling-tube.   Rinse the beaker with several small amounts of hot distilled water, pouring each successive amount of water over the filter-paper to wash it thoroughly; collect the filtered washings in the boiling-tube.   Continue this procedure until the volume of solution in the tube is 25 ml.   Add 5·0 ml of acid ammonium molybdate and 5·0 ml of Metol - sulphite solution.   Immerse the tube in a boiling-water bath for 30 minutes and then cool the contents to room temperature.

Transfer the contents of the tube to a 50-ml calibrated flask and dilute to the mark with distilled water.   Measure the optical density of the solution in a 4-cm cell, using a spectrophotometer at a wavelength of 6500 A, or in an absorptiometer with a suitable red filter.   Use water in the comparison cell.   From a previously prepared calibration graph (see later) read the concentration, in milligrams per litre, of Lissapol NX corresponding to the observed optical density.

Alternatively, the colours may be compared with proprietary coloured discs in a suitable instrument; for example, the B.D.H. Nessleriser, and Tschopps's phosphate disc C, can be used after the following procedure: transfer the cooled solution to a Nessler cylinder and dilute to 50 ml with distilled water; fill the comparison tube with a solution prepared by heating together 5 ml of acid ammonium molybdate solution, 5 ml of Metol - sulphite solution, 25 ml of distilled water and 1 ml of diluted sulphuric acid (1 + 1), for 30 minutes, as in an actual test.

The following concentrations of Lissapol NX have been found to correspond to the disc markings—

Amount of phosphate (read from disc), µg	15	30	45
Lissapol NX (40-ml sample without deproteinisation), mg per litre	5	10	15
Lissapol NX (40-ml sample with deproteinisation), mg per litre ..	7	14	21

Poor-quality effluents and crude sewages—

Measure from a 100-ml graduated cylinder 80 ml of the sample into a 250-ml beaker.   Add from a graduated cylinder 10 ml of 5 per cent. zinc sulphate solution, swirl to mix the solution, and then add slowly, with swirling, 10 ml of barium hydroxide solution. Heat just to boiling, cool rapidly to room temperature, and then filter through a 12·5-cm filter-paper (Whatman No. 1 paper is suitable). Measure 50·0 ml of the clear filtrate (see Note 2) into a separating funnel containing 15 g of sodium chloride and proceed as described under "Clear effluents" from "Add 10 ml of ether measured with a graduated cylinder, . . ."

PREPARATION OF CALIBRATION GRAPHS—

Standard solution of Lissapol NX—Into a 100-ml beaker weigh 0·40 ± 0·01 g of Lissapol NX. Add about 20 ml of distilled water and stir, with gentle heating, until the material is freely dispersed. Allow to cool and then dilute with water to 1 litre in a calibrated flask. The weight of Lissapol NX present in 1 ml of this solution if present in a 40-ml sample (see Note 2) of effluent would correspond to a concentration of 10 mg of Lissapol NX per litre.

(a) *Preparation of graph for use with samples that have not been deproteinised before extraction with ether*—Into a series of 15-ml centrifuge tubes measure x ml of standard Lissapol NX solution ($x = 0·5, 1·0, 1·5, 2·0, 2·5$ and $3·0$) from a burette, $(3 - x)$ ml of distilled water, 0·5 ml of absolute ethanol, 1 ml of diluted hydrochloric acid $(1 + 1)$, 0·5 ml of barium chloride solution and 2·0 ml of molybdophosphoric acid solution. Then proceed as described under "Clear effluents," from "Stir the contents of the tube with a glass rod . . ." Construct a graph relating the Lissapol NX content—expressed as milligrams per litre on a 40-ml test sample—to the optical density, measured either with an ultra-violet spectrophotometer or with an absorptiometer, as may be appropriate.

(b) *Preparation of graph for use with samples that have been deproteinised with zinc sulphate and barium hydroxide before extraction with ether*—Measure carefully into a series of 250-ml beakers from a burette x ml of standard Lissapol NX solution ($x = 1, 2, 3, 4$ and 6) and $(80 - x)$ ml of water. Then proceed as described under "Poor quality effluents and crude sewages," from the words "Add 10 ml of 5 per cent. zinc sulphate solution . . ." Construct a graph relating the Lissapol NX content—expressed as milligrams per litre on a 40-ml test sample—to the optical density measured either with an ultra-violet spectrophotometer or with an absorptiometer, as may be appropriate.

NOTES—1. This method for Lissapol N-type detergents depends on the determination of the phosphate content of the Lissapol N - barium - molybdophosphoric acid complex. The weight of complex isolated from unit weight of Lissapol NX is constant. It has therefore been assumed that the ratio of phosphorus to Lissapol NX in the complex is also constant.

2. Fifty millilitres of the deproteinised filtrate are equivalent to 40 ml of the original sample.

3. Most domestic detergents contain diluents in the form of inorganic salts or water or both, the active agent content not being disclosed. In consequence, the normal practice in recent publications on this subject is to express the detergent content as mg of active agent per litre and *not* mg of the detergent as marketed per litre. This practice has been followed in the foregoing method.

ANION- AND CATION-ACTIVE SUBSTANCES IN ADMIXTURE
(TENTATIVE METHOD)

When anionic and cationic surface-active agents are present together, the foregoing methods will give only a measure of the extent to which one is in excess of the other.

The following methods[8] are intended to measure the total content of each form:

however, apart from the use of a resin to separate the two forms, no new principle or method is involved.

NOTE—The column of resin may give a blank value of up to 1 p.p.m. of anion-active material on being washed with 100 ml of water; the washings may be tinted violet.

(a) DETERMINATION OF ANION-ACTIVE MATERIAL IN PRESENCE OF CATION-ACTIVE MATERIAL

The following method is appropriate no matter which form is present in excess.

PRINCIPLE OF METHOD—

When a solution containing anion- and cation-active substances is passed through a column of a cation-exchange resin, for example, Zeo-Karb 225, the cation-active material is absorbed.

PROCEDURE—

In a tube 1 cm in diameter prepare a column of resin 30 cm long; this will serve for several estimations.

Pass 20 ml of the sample through the column, taking 20 minutes for the operation. Wash the column with three 20-ml portions of distilled water; the time of passage for the last washing can be reduced to 10 minutes.

(b) ESTIMATION OF CATION-ACTIVE MATERIAL IN PRESENCE OF AN EXCESS OF ANION-ACTIVE MATERIAL

PROCEDURE—

(i) A determination of anion-active material is carried out directly on the sample, by one of the methods previously described.

The difference between this result and that obtained in (a) above gives a very approximate indication of cationic content equivalent to the difference in anionic strength by the two methods.

(ii) A more correct estimate is obtained by passing a portion of sample through a resin column as in (a). Then treat the percolate with a standard solution of cation-active material until the same result is obtained as in the direct estimation on the sample. A fairly good estimate in terms of cation-active material can thus be obtained.

(c) ESTIMATION OF CATION-ACTIVE MATERIAL IN PRESENCE OF A SLIGHT EXCESS OR LESS ANION-ACTIVE MATERIAL

Again remove the cationic material by passing the sample through a resin column as before and determine the anion-active material alone. This amount of anion-active material is then included in the excess used to determine the cation-active material directly on the sample by the method given for determination of Cationic Detergents.

REFERENCES

1. Longwell, J., and Maniece, W. D., *Analyst*, 1955, **80**, 167.
2. Epton, S. R., *Trans. Faraday Soc.*, 1948, **44**, 226.
3. Barr, T., Oliver, J., and Stubbings, W. V., *J. Soc. Chem. Ind.*, 1948, **67**, 45; *Analyst*, 1951, **76**, 283.
4. Finch, H. J., private communication.
5. Degens, P. N., Evans, H. C., Kommer, J. D., and Winsor, P. A., *J. Appl. Chem.*, 1953, **3**, 54.
6. Heatley, N. G., and Page, E. J., *Wat. & Sanitary Engineer*, 1952, **3**, 46.
7. Schaffer, C. B., and Critchfield, F. N., *Anal. Chem.*, 1947, **19**, 32.
8. Finch, H. J., personal communication.

Fluoride

PRINCIPLE OF METHOD—

In this method,[1] after removal of free chlorine by arsenite, fluorine is steam-distilled as hydrofluorosilicic acid in the presence of perchloric acid; the fluoride ion is determined by titration, which depends on the bleaching action of fluoride on the thorium lake of alizarin red S.

RANGE—

For fluoride contents (as F′) between 0·5 and 5 mg per litre of sample.

APPLICABILITY—

The method is generally applicable.

APPARATUS—

Distillation apparatus—The apparatus, of borosilicate glass, consists of a 100-ml Claissen flask connected to a water-cooled condenser by means of the side-tube. The neck carries a thermometer and a steam-inlet tube, both reaching nearly to the bottom of the flask.

The water used for steam generation *must* be made alkaline with sodium hydroxide.

REAGENTS—

Sodium arsenite solution, 1 *per cent. w/v.*
Perchloric acid, 60 *per cent.*
Hydrochloric acid, 0·05 N.
Sodium hydroxide solution, 0·05 N.
Thorium nitrate solution—Dissolve 0·25 g of thorium nitrate, $Th(NO_3)_4.4H_2O$, in distilled water and dilute to 1 litre.
Alizarin red S solution, 0·01 *per cent.*
Standard fluoride solution—Dissolve 0·221 g of dry sodium fluoride in distilled water and dilute to 100 ml. Dilute 10·0 ml of this solution to 1 litre.

$$1 \text{ ml} \equiv 0·01 \text{ mg of fluoride (as F′).}$$

Silver sulphate.
Calcium oxide (fluoride-free)—This can be prepared by the following method—

Prepare an ammonium carbonate reagent by dissolving 110 g of ammonium carbonate (analytical-reagent grade) and 55 ml of ammonium hydroxide, sp.gr. 0·880, in distilled water and diluting to 600 ml.

Dissolve 200 g of dry calcium chloride (analytical-reagent grade) in about 600 ml of warm distilled water. Stir into this solution 20 ml of ammonium carbonate reagent, bring the mixture just to the boiling-point, allow the precipitate to settle for a few minutes and filter it on a Buchner funnel, using suction. Reject the precipitate. Repeat the precipitation and filtration three times, using 20 ml of ammonium carbonate reagent each time. Finally, treat the clear filtrate from the last precipitation with the remainder of the ammonium carbonate reagent, stir the mixture well and bring it just to the boiling-point. Allow the precipitate to settle, filter and wash it several times with hot distilled water until free from chloride. Dry it at 100° C and ignite to oxide in a platinum dish in small quantities of 1 to 2 g as required.

Methyl orange indicator solution—A 0·04 per cent. w/v aqueous solution.

(*a*) PROCEDURE FOR EFFLUENTS KNOWN TO BE FREE FROM APPRECIABLE AMOUNTS OF ORGANIC MATTER—

Remove any free chlorine by adding sufficient (but not an excess of) sodium arsenite solution.

H̄

Preparation of apparatus—Into the Claissen flask measure 0·2 g of silver sulphate (see Note), 7 ml of distilled water and 15 ml of perchloric acid, and add a number of fragments of borosilicate glass (or glass wool if "bumping" is experienced). Heat the flask until the temperature reaches 120° to 125° C, connect the steam supply and distil the contents at a temperature of 137° to 140° C. Distil 150 ml during 25 to 35 minutes, steam out the condenser and discard the distillate.

Determination of blank—Proceed to steam-distil a further 150 ml, and determine the fluoride in the distillate by the method described below. The figure for the blank should not exceed 0·0015 mg of fluoride and should remain approximately constant for further 150-ml fractions.

Determination of fluoride—Cool the contents of the flask and add 20 ml of the effluent sample, rinsing the neck of the flask with 1 or 2 ml of distilled water. Connect the steam supply and distil 150 ml as described above.

Determine the acidity of the distillate as follows—

In a 100-ml Nessler cylinder, titrate 50 ml of the well mixed distillate with 0·05 N sodium hydroxide solution, using a drop of methyl orange indicator solution, until the colour matches that in a similar cylinder containing an equal volume of distilled water and a drop of methyl orange indicator solution.

Transfer the remaining 100 ml of distillate (or a suitable aliquot diluted to 100 ml, if the fluoride content is high) to a Nessler cylinder and add the requisite amount of 0·05 N hydrochloric acid to make the total acidity equal to 5·0 ml of 0·05 N acid. Prepare a control cylinder containing 5·0 ml of 0·05 N hydrochloric acid diluted to the same volume with distilled water, and add to both cylinders 3 ml of alizarin red S solution. To the test cylinder add thorium nitrate solution from a burette until a slight pink colour persists when compared with the yellow of the control cylinder. Add an exactly similar volume of thorium nitrate solution to the control cylinder, which then becomes more pink than the test cylinder; then add slowly from a burette (graduated at 0·02-ml intervals) standard fluoride solution until the tints of the test and control solutions match. The volume of standard fluoride solution added corresponds to the amount of fluoride present in the portion of test distillate taken.

Calculate the amount of fluoride present in 150 ml of distillate, subtract the figure obtained for the blank and express the net fluoride content as milligrams per litre of sample.

(*b*) PROCEDURE FOR EFFLUENTS CONTAINING APPRECIABLE AMOUNTS OF ORGANIC
      MATTER—

Measure 20 ml of the effluent sample into a platinum basin, add 1 g of fluoride-free calcium oxide and evaporate the contents to dryness on a water bath. Transfer the basin and residue to a muffle furnace maintained at approximately 600° C, ignite for 1½ to 2 hours, and cool. Using not more than 20 ml of distilled water acidified with perchloric acid, wash the contents of the basin into the distillation flask and proceed to determine the fluoride content as described under (*a*) above.

NOTE—The silver sulphate added must be in excess of the equivalent amount of chloride present in the effluent and more than 0·2 g should be added if necessary.

REFERENCE

1. Analytical Methods Committee, *Analyst*, 1944, **69**, 243.

Formaldehyde

PRINCIPLE OF METHOD—

In this method,[1] the formaldehyde reacts with acetylacetone in the presence of an excess of an ammonium salt to form a yellow compound, diacetyldihydrolutidine, which is determined colorimetrically.

RANGE—

For formaldehyde contents up to 8 mg per litre of sample.

APPLICABILITY—

Distillation of the sample is included to reduce interference. A full investigation of interfering substances has not been made, but it is known that phenols up to 200 mg per litre do not interfere.

REAGENTS—

Acetylacetone reagent—Dissolve 150 g of ammonium acetate in distilled water, add 3 ml of glacial acetic acid and 2 ml of acetylacetone, and dilute to 1 litre with distilled water.

Sodium sulphite solution—Dissolve 250 g of sodium sulphite, $Na_2SO_3.7H_2O$, in 1 litre of distilled water.

Sulphuric acid, 1·0 N.

Standard formaldehyde solution—Determine the formaldehyde content of technical formaldehyde solution (about 40 per cent. w/w of formaldehyde) as follows—

Weigh about 6 g of technical formaldehyde solution into a 100-ml calibrated flask and dilute to the mark with distilled water. Measure 25 ml from a pipette into a 250-ml flask, add a drop of thymolphthalein indicator solution and neutralise with N sodium hydroxide solution. Add 2 drops of thymolphthalein indicator solution to 50 ml of sodium sulphite solution and neutralise it. Add this sodium sulphite solution to the neutralised formaldehyde solution, mix and titrate the liberated sodium hydroxide with 1·0 N sulphuric acid.

1 ml of 1·0 N sulphuric acid ≡ 0·03003 g of formaldehyde.

Calculate the formaldehyde content of the diluted formaldehyde solution, and immediately before use prepare a solution such that—

1 ml ≡ 0·1 mg of formaldehyde.

Thymolphthalein indicator solution—A 0·1 per cent. solution in ethanol.

PROCEDURE—

Transfer 50 ml of the effluent sample (containing not more than 8 mg of formaldehyde per litre) to a 100-ml flask. Acidify slightly with dilute sulphuric acid and add 10 ml of distilled water. Connect the flask by means of a glass joint to a water-cooled condenser and distil 50 ml of the solution into a 100-ml measuring cylinder. Add 50 ml of acetylacetone reagent, and transfer the mixture to a stoppered flask and heat it at 60° C for 10 minutes.

Carry out a blank procedure on all the reagents used.

Cool the solutions and measure the optical densities in a spectrophotometer or in an absorptiometer, using a 1-cm cell and using a wavelength of 4250 A in a spectrophotometer or a suitable violet filter in an absorptiometer. Use distilled water in the comparison cell. Read the number of milligrams of formaldehyde equivalent to the observed optical densities of the test and blank solutions from a previously prepared calibration graph, and so obtain the net measure of formaldehyde in the sample.

Express the result as milligrams of formaldehyde per litre of sample.

Establish the calibration graph as follows—

Into a series of stoppered flasks measure appropriate amounts of the diluted standard formaldehyde solution, covering the range 0 to 8 mg of formaldehyde per litre, and dilute each to 50 ml. Add 50 ml of acetylacetone reagent and proceed as for the sample. Measure the optical densities, using a 1-cm cell, and construct a graph relating the optical densities to the number of milligrams of formaldehyde.

NOTE—If the effluent sample contains more than 8 mg of formaldehyde per litre, dilute appropriately.

REFERENCE

1. Nash, T., *Biochem. J.*, 1953, **55**, 416.

Combined Nitrogen

Combined nitrogen occurs in effluents in several forms, and the methods of determination are given under the following headings, which are indicative of the mode of combination—

Ammoniacal nitrogen (free and saline ammonia).
Albuminoid nitrogen.
Organic nitrogen.
Total unoxidised nitrogen.
Nitrogen present as nitrite.
Nitrogen present as nitrate.

The terms "free" and "fixed" ammonia are frequently used in connection with ammoniacal gas liquors. "Free" ammonia is that derived on boiling the sample directly; "fixed" ammonia is that liberated on boiling, after addition of alkali, the liquid from which the "free" ammonia has first been removed. When ammoniacal liquors occur as pollutants in an effluent, this distinction ceases to be of importance, and the free and the fixed ammonia are determined together as *ammoniacal nitrogen*.

Albuminoid nitrogen is defined as the nitrogen converted to ammonia by oxidation of organic matter with an alkaline solution of potassium permanganate.

Organic nitrogen represents the total nitrogen of organic compounds, of which albuminoid nitrogen is a part.

Total unoxidised nitrogen includes nitrogen present in all forms other than nitrite and nitrate. This ought to be equivalent to the sum of the ammoniacal nitrogen plus the organic nitrogen; however, as noted in the text, the separate determination of the organic nitrogen in effluents is liable to give low results. Therefore, some stress is laid upon the importance of a direct determination of the total unoxidised nitrogen.

In general, the methods of determination consist in converting nitrogen to ammonia, removing ammonia from the sample by distillation and determining the ammonia either by nesslerisation or titration.

All results are expressed in terms of "nitrogen," as milligrams per litre of sample.

Whenever combined nitrogen in one or other of its forms is determined as ammonia, the analysis should be made in an atmosphere free from ammonia. In particular, bottles containing solutions of ammonia should not be kept in the room where the analysis is carried out.

In order to maintain uniformity in practice, several of the methods described below are substantially the same as those given in "Methods of Chemical Analysis as Applied to Sewage and Sewage Effluents," published for the Ministry of Housing and Local Government by H.M. Stationery Office.

AMMONIACAL NITROGEN

Two methods are recommended, a distillation and nesslerisation method for minute amounts of nitrogen and a distillation and titration method for larger amounts.

DISTILLATION AND NESSLERISATION METHOD

PRINCIPLE OF METHOD—

The method of determination consists in matching, visually or instrumentally, (a) the colour produced on adding a suitable quantity of Nessler reagent to a measured volume of distillate with (b) the colour of a similarly nesslerised solution containing a known amount of standard dilute ammonium chloride solution; the two solutions must be as nearly as possible at the same temperature, preferably between 15° and 20° C.

APPARATUS—

A *round-bottomed borosilicate-glass flask*, having a capacity of 1 litre and fitted with an anti-splash bulb and a suitable condenser, which may be of the spiral-tube type in borosilicate glass, tin or silver.

Glass vessels, having a capacity of about 300 ml and marked at 240 ml, for collection of the distillates.

Nessler cylinders of nominal capacity 100 *ml*—As specified in British Standard 612.

Before assembling the apparatus, clean the distilling flask, anti-splash bulb and condensing tube carefully and thoroughly; afterwards, in order to free the apparatus from residual traces of ammonia, pour into the flask about 500 ml of distilled water, preferably free from ammonia, and distil until the distillate is shown to be free from ammonia by tests with Nessler reagent.

REAGENTS—

Ammonia-free distilled water—This is prepared from tap-water, but the procedure is different when the tap-water contains free chlorine.

> *Method (i): Preparation from tap-water containing no free chlorine*—To tap-water contained in a round-bottomed borosilicate-glass flask (having a capacity of 1 to 2 litres), add sufficient dilute sulphuric acid to make the water slightly acid to methyl orange, and then a crystal of potassium permanganate. To the neck of the flask fit an anti-splash bulb and connect the whole to a condenser. Distil with care, collecting the distillate as soon as it has been shown, by testing with Nessler reagent, to be free from ammonia. A deposit of manganese dioxide may gradually settle and should be removed between distillations in order to avoid "bumping."

> *Method (ii): Preparation from tap-water containing free chlorine*—To each litre of tap-water add 2 ml of a 10 per cent. solution of ferrous sulphate and sufficient sulphuric acid to give an acid reaction to methyl orange. Distil with care, using the anti-splash bulb, as described above, until one quarter of the volume remains.

Standard ammonium chloride solution A—Dissolve 3·82 g of pure dried ammonium chloride in distilled water and dilute to 1 litre, using ammonia-free distilled water.

1 ml ≡ 1 mg of ammoniacal nitrogen.

Dilute standard ammonium chloride solution B—Dilute 10 ml of solution A to 1 litre with ammonia-free distilled water.   Prepare this solution freshly at frequent intervals.

$$1 \text{ ml} \equiv 0.01 \text{ mg of ammoniacal nitrogen.}$$

Nessler reagent—Dissolve 35 g of potassium iodide and 12·5 g of mercuric chloride in 300 ml of water, and add a saturated aqueous solution of mercuric chloride until a slight permanent precipitate is formed (about 44 ml will be required).   Then add gradually, with frequent shaking, a solution (cooled to room temperature) of 120 g of sodium hydroxide in 150 ml of water.   When the mixture has again cooled, add a further 1 ml of the saturated mercuric chloride solution and shake the mixture. Finally, dilute the mixture to 1 litre, shake it again and allow it to settle for at least 24 hours.   Only the clear supernatant liquid should be used in the test.   The solution is preferably stored in a rubber-stoppered bottle in the dark and only a portion of the clear supernatant liquid is transferred periodically to a small bottle for current use.

Sodium carbonate solution—A solution containing 2·5 g of sodium carbonate, Na_2CO_3, in 100 ml of distilled water.

PROCEDURE—

Size of sample—The volume of sample required in the test depends on the amount of ammonia present.   For effluents containing 30 to 50 mg per litre of ammoniacal nitrogen, a suitable volume is 25 ml; for those containing substantially less, a correspondingly larger volume should be used.   With effluents of high ammonia content, a preliminary dilution should be made with ammonia-free distilled water and a suitable aliquot taken for the test.

Distillation—After freeing the distillation apparatus from ammonia, empty the distilling flask and, when cool, measure into it the required volume of sample. If the sample is acid, neutralise to phenolphthalein with sodium carbonate solution; to the neutral liquid add 1 ml of sodium carbonate solution and sufficient ammonia-free distilled water to bring the volume to 500 ml.   Connect the flask to the anti-splash bulb and the condenser, bring the contents quickly to the boil and distil at a rate of about 10 ml per minute, collecting 240 ml of distillate.   Transfer the distillate to a 250-ml calibrated flask, dilute to the mark with ammonia-free distilled water and mix well.   Continue the distillation, collecting 50-ml portions and estimating the ammoniacal nitrogen content of each by means of Nessler reagent, until the whole of the ammonia has been evolved.   Usually, all the ammonia is found in the main distillate.

Determine the ammoniacal nitrogen present in the main distillate by measurement of the colour developed after the addition of Nessler reagent, as described below.   The colour may be measured either visually or instrumentally.

Express the result as milligrams of ammoniacal nitrogen per litre of sample.

Visual colour-comparison method—Into a series of matched 50-ml Nessler cylinders measure volumes between 0 and 5·0 ml of dilute standard ammonium chloride solution B.   Into another similar Nessler cylinder measure 50 ml of the distillate (or a smaller measured volume diluted to 50 ml with ammonia-free distilled water).   Fill all the cylinders to the 50-ml mark with ammonia-free distilled water, and to each add 2 ml of Nessler reagent; mix gently.   Allow 10 minutes for the colour to develop and compare the colour produced by the sample with those of the standards.   If the colour of the nesslerised distillate is more intense than that of the highest standard, repeat with a smaller volume of distillate.   Dilution is not recommended once the Nessler reagent has been added.

Since 1 ml of standard ammonium chloride solution B is equivalent to 0·01 mg of nitrogen, then, if x ml of sample have been taken for distillation, 250 ml of the distillate have been collected, and if y ml of the distillate have been found to be equal to z ml of the standard—

$$\text{Ammoniacal nitrogen (mg per litre)} = \frac{2500\,z}{xy}.$$

To this figure should be added the figure for ammoniacal nitrogen collected in subsequent portions, if any, of the distillate.

The matching of the colour produced by Nessler reagent can also be made with standard tinted-glass discs that can be purchased. It should be noted that the disc readings are often given as ammonia, whereas the result should be recorded as nitrogen. This method has many advantages, but it is essential to prepare and use the Nessler reagent exactly in accordance with the instructions of the manufacturers of the discs. Further, each time a Nessler reagent is prepared it should be checked against standard ammonium chloride solution to ascertain whether the colours produced accord with those of the discs at the appropriate concentrations of ammonia. If not, a correction factor is necessary.

Instrumental method—The optical density of the colour may also be measured in a spectrophotometer or in an absorptiometer, using a cell of appropriate size and using a wavelength of 4670 A in a spectrophotometer or a suitable blue filter in an absorptiometer. Use water in the comparison cell. Read the number of milligrams of ammoniacal nitrogen equivalent to the observed optical density of the test solution from a previously prepared calibration graph, and so obtain the net measure of ammoniacal nitrogen in the sample.

Establish the calibration graph as follows—

Dilute appropriate measured amounts of dilute standard ammonium chloride solution B to 100 ml with ammonia-free distilled water and add to each dilution 4 ml of Nessler reagent, mix and allow to stand for 10 minutes. Measure the optical densities and construct a graph relating the optical densities to the number of milligrams of ammoniacal nitrogen.

DISTILLATION AND TITRATION METHOD

PRINCIPLE OF METHOD—

In this method[1] the ammonia is distilled into a measured volume of standard sulphuric acid, the acid in excess of that required for neutralisation of the ammonia being determined by titration with standard sodium hydroxide.

APPARATUS—

The apparatus required is similar to that described under "Distillation and Nesslerisation Method," but the distilling flask need only have a capacity of 750 ml, and a double splash-head is recommended. A vertical borosilicate-glass condenser is suitable. The receiving vessel should preferably be conical and have a capacity of about 350 ml.

REAGENTS—

Sulphuric acid, N, *nitrogen-free*.

Sulphuric acid, 0·01 N—Dilute 10·0 ml of the N acid to 1 litre with freshly boiled and cooled ammonia-free distilled water. Store in a borosilicate-glass bottle.

Sodium hydroxide solution, N.

Sodium hydroxide solution, 0·01 N—Dilute 10·0 ml of the N solution to 1 litre with freshly boiled and cooled ammonia-free distilled water. Store in a borosilicate-glass aspirator fitted with a one-holed rubber stopper and provided with a suitable means for excluding atmospheric carbon dioxide, *e.g.*, a U-tube with a soda-lime guard-tube attached.   Prepare this solution freshly at frequent intervals.

Methylene blue - methyl red indicator solution—To 100 ml of a 0·1 per cent. solution of methyl red in neutral ethanol add 25 ml of a 0·1 per cent. solution of methylene blue in neutral ethanol.

Light magnesium oxide.

PROCEDURE—

After freeing the apparatus from ammonia, measure into the empty and cooled distilling flask the required volume of effluent sample (previously neutralised to phenolphthalein, if necessary), preferably containing between 0·3 and 7 mg of ammoniacal nitrogen.   Dilute to 350 ml with ammonia-free distilled water, add 0·25 g of light magnesium oxide, and connect the flask to the splash-head and condenser.   Place the receiving flask, containing 50·0 ml of 0·01 *N* sulphuric acid and 6 drops of methylene blue - methyl red indicator solution, below the condenser so that the end of the condenser tube reaches to the bottom of the flask.   Distil at the rate of 5 to 10 ml per minute until at least 150 ml have distilled over.   Boil the contents of the receiving flask and titrate hot with 0·01 *N* sodium hydroxide solution to a green end-point.

Blank determinations should be carried out occasionally and a correction made to the final titration figure for any ammonia in the reagents used.

Express the result as milligrams of ammoniacal nitrogen per litre of sample.

1 ml of 0·01 *N* sulphuric acid $\equiv$ 0·14 mg of ammoniacal nitrogen.

Separate determinations of "free" and "fixed" ammonia

(*a*) *"Free" ammonia*—This may be determined by either of the foregoing methods for the determination of ammoniacal nitrogen, *omitting* the addition of sodium carbonate solution or light magnesium oxide to the effluent in the distilling flask.

(*b*) *"Fixed" ammonia*—After distillation of the "free" ammonia as described in (*a*) above, allow the contents of the distilling flask to cool; then add 1 ml of sodium carbonate solution or 0·25 g of light magnesium oxide, according to the method being used, and a volume of ammonia-free distilled water equal to that removed in the distillation of the "free" ammonia.   Proceed with the distillation and determination of ammoniacal nitrogen as "fixed" ammonia.

> NOTE—In some chlorinated effluents interference may occur in the determinations made by the above methods.   In the light of present knowledge no specific instructions can be formulated which will deal with every such case and hence only a general warning can be given.   If the ammoniacal nitrogen content of a chlorinated effluent (or of a flow containing chlorinated effluent) is important, each such sample must be investigated and the degree of interference ascertained before the true result can be arrived at.

ALBUMINOID NITROGEN

This determination is of value in the analysis of sewage and sewage effluents, as it affords a measure of the more readily decomposable nitrogenous organic matter present.   Its use in connection with trade effluents is mainly for the purpose of relating the character of the trade effluent to that of sewage.

The determination is carried out on the residue after distillation for the determination of "Ammoniacal Nitrogen" by the distillation and nesslerisation method.

REAGENTS—

In addition to the reagents listed under "Ammoniacal Nitrogen" nesslerisation method the following is required.

Alkaline potassium permanganate solution—Dissolve 8 g of potassium permanganate in 200 ml of distilled water and separately dissolve 150 g of sodium hydroxide in 500 ml of distilled water. Mix the solutions. Dilute to about 1 litre with distilled water and boil the solution gently (preferably in an enamelled iron vessel) until the volume is reduced to about 500 ml. After cooling, dilute to 1 litre with ammonia-free distilled water.

The permanganate solution so prepared should not evolve any ammonia when tested by adding 25 ml of the solution to 250 ml of ammonia-free distilled water, distilling, and nesslerising the first 50 ml of the distillate.

PROCEDURE—

Carry out the determination on the residue after distillation for the determination of ammoniacal nitrogen (nesslerisation method).

When the residue has cooled somewhat, add 40 ml of alkaline potassium permanganate solution; then resume distillation at a rate of about 10 ml per minute and collect the distillate. Should the colour of the permanganate be destroyed on boiling, repeat the determination on a smaller quantity of sample.

Collect a number of separate fractions, *e.g.*, of 100 ml, 50 ml and 50 ml, and determine the ammonia in each by nesslerisation as described for the determination of ammoniacal nitrogen.

NOTE—Traces of ammonia in diminishing amounts are often obtained in successive fractions and experience with particular types of samples will indicate how much distillate is necessary; usually 200 ml will suffice.

Express the result as milligrams of albuminoid nitrogen per litre of sample.

ORGANIC NITROGEN

PRINCIPLE OF METHOD—

In this method,[2] any nitrite or nitrate in the effluent sample is first reduced to ammonia, which, together with any ammoniacal nitrogen already present in the sample, is removed by evaporation of the slightly alkaline solution. The organic nitrogen is then converted into ammonia by the Kjeldahl method and, after distillation, determined either by nesslerisation or titration.

Some effluents may contain organic nitrogen compounds that are not completely converted into ammonia by the Kjeldahl digestion. For example, it has been stated that nitro-, nitroso-, hydrazo-, azo- and azoxy-compounds, oximes and hydrazines are not satisfactorily converted and that cyclic nitrogen compounds, particularly those containing a pyridine ring, are only slowly broken down. It has been reported[3] that azo-, nitro- and nitroso-compounds can be satisfactorily reduced if glucose is added to the digestion mixture. Complete conversion of pyridine-ring compounds is said to require digestion for 3 to 4 hours with sulphuric acid in the presence of selenium oxychloride and metallic mercury as catalysts.[4] For compounds not amenable to either of these procedures, reduction with hydriodic acid and red phosphorus has been used.[5]

REAGENTS—

In addition to the reagents listed under "Ammoniacal Nitrogen" (nesslerisation and titration methods), the following are required.

Devarda's alloy, powdered—This must be as free from nitrogen as possible and fine enough to pass through a 200-mesh sieve.

Sodium hydroxide solution, approximately 40 *per cent.*—Dissolve 1500 g of pure ammonia-free sodium hydroxide in 3 litres of distilled water in an enamelled or stainless-steel vessel and boil gently for half an hour to remove any traces of ammonia.

I

Sulphuric acid, sp.gr. 1·84, *nitrogen-free.*
Phenolphthalein indicator solution, 0·1 *per cent. in* 50 *per cent. ethanol.*

PROCEDURE—

Place the required amount of effluent sample, preferably at least 100 ml (more if the content of organic nitrogen is expected to be very low), in a 300 to 350-ml round-bottomed borosilicate-glass flask having a short neck.   Add 0·5 g of Devarda's alloy and 0·25 to 0·35 ml of 40 per cent. sodium hydroxide solution, and cautiously bring the whole to the boil.   At the boiling-point considerable frothing is likely to occur.   This should be avoided and care must be taken to prevent loss.   Continue boiling until only 5 to 10 ml of liquid remain.   Cool; then add 10 ml of sulphuric acid, sp. gr. 1·84, and boil the mixture fairly briskly.   Continue boiling for 10 minutes after the liquid has become colourless or pale green.   After cooling, add about 150 ml of ammonia-free distilled water, with continuous mixing to avoid local over-heating. Transfer the solution to a 1-litre flask, rinse the reaction flask two or three times with ammonia-free distilled water, using sufficient to dissolve any solid sulphate present, and transfer the rinsings to the larger flask.   Bring the total volume to about 500 ml with ammonia-free distilled water.   Add a few drops of phenolphthalein indicator solution and, taking care to keep the mixture cool to avoid loss of ammonia, add sufficient 40 per cent. sodium hydroxide solution to produce a permanent pink colour. Distil off the ammonia and determine it by one of the methods described under "Ammoniacal Nitrogen," according to the amount of nitrogen present.

Blank determinations should be carried out on the reagents and a correction made for any ammonia found.

Express the result as milligrams of organic nitrogen per litre of sample.

TOTAL UNOXIDISED NITROGEN

METHOD A—IN ABSENCE OF NITRITE AND NITRATE

A measurement of the total nitrogen present in an effluent free from nitrite and nitrate is often made by separate determinations of the ammoniacal nitrogen and of the organic nitrogen and adding the amounts of the constituents found.

In certain instances, however, the sum of the results of these determinations is somewhat less than the result of a direct determination of the total nitrogen, because of the simultaneous distillation of certain undecomposed volatile nitrogenous compounds with the ammonia in the determination of ammoniacal nitrogen.   Consequently, it is preferable to determine the total nitrogen present in such effluents directly by the Kjeldahl method.

REAGENTS—

In addition to the reagents listed under "Ammoniacal Nitrogen" (nesslerisation and titration methods) and "Organic Nitrogen," the following is required.

Sodium sulphate - copper sulphate mixture—Mix thoroughly, by grinding, 500 parts of anhydrous sodium sulphate and 8 parts of anhydrous copper sulphate.

PROCEDURE—

This is similar in many respects to that recommended for the determination of organic nitrogen.

Place the required amount of the effluent sample, *e.g.*, 100 ml, in a 300 to 350-ml round-bottomed borosilicate-glass flask having a short neck.   Add 6 g of sodium sulphate - copper sulphate mixture and, with care and frequent shaking, 25 ml of sulphuric acid, sp. gr. 1·84.   Boil the mixture gently at first to expel water; then continue the boiling briskly.   Continue boiling the liquid for 10 minutes after the liquid has become pale green. After cooling, add about 150 ml of ammonia-free distilled water, with continuous mixing to avoid local over-heating. Transfer the solution to a 1-litre flask, rinse the reaction flask two or three times with ammonia-free distilled water, using sufficient to dissolve any solid sulphate present, and transfer the rinsings to the larger flask. Bring the total volume to about 500 ml with ammonia-free distilled water. Add a few drops of phenolphthalein indicator solution and, taking care to keep the mixture cool to avoid loss of ammonia, sufficient 40 per cent. sodium hydroxide solution to produce a permanent pink colour. Distil off the ammonia and determine it by one of the methods described under "Ammoniacal Nitrogen," according to the amount of nitrogen present, taking care to prevent excessive boiling of the solution at the commencement of the distillation.

Blank determinations should be carried out on the reagents and a correction made for any ammonia found.

Express the result as milligrams of total unoxidised nitrogen per litre of sample.

METHOD B—IN PRESENCE OF NITRITE AND NITRATE

The determination of total unoxidised nitrogen in the presence of oxidised forms cannot be readily accomplished. It is more satisfactory to reduce the oxidised forms present to ammonia, by some means such as Devarda's alloy (as described under "Organic Nitrogen"), boil off the ammonia so formed, together with the ammoniacal nitrogen originally present in the sample, and then to determine, by the Kjeldahl method described above, the organic nitrogen present in the residue.

The total unoxidised nitrogen is then taken to be the sum of the ammoniacal nitrogen and the organic nitrogen determined as described above.

NITROGEN PRESENT AS NITRITE
(GRIESS - ILOSVAY METHOD)

PRINCIPLE OF METHOD—

The method depends upon the formation of a pink azo dye when the diazonium compound formed by the action of nitrous acid on sulphanilic acid is coupled with 1-naphthylamine.

RANGE—

For nitrite nitrogen contents of up to 2 mg per litre.

REAGENTS

Sulphanilic acid solution—Dissolve 8·0 g of sulphanilic acid in 570 ml of warm diluted acetic acid (1 + 1). When solution is complete, dilute to 1 litre with distilled water.

1-Naphthylamine solution—Dissolve 2·5 g of solid 1-naphthylamine in 290 ml of diluted acetic acid (1 + 1), warming to effect solution if necessary. When solution is complete, dilute to 500 ml with distilled water. Discard this solution when it becomes markedly discoloured.

Standard nitrite solution A—Dissolve 0·247 g of sodium nitrite* in freshly boiled and cooled distilled water and dilute the solution to 1 litre. If kept in the dark, the solution is stable for some months.

1 ml ≡ 0·05 mg of nitrite nitrogen.

Dilute standard nitrite solution B—Dilute 10·0 ml of nitrite solution A to 1 litre with distilled water. This solution is not stable and must be freshly prepared.

1 ml ≡ 0·5 μg of nitrite nitrogen.

* Sodium nitrite of analytical-reagent quality is only guaranteed to be 98 per cent. pure and, for extreme accuracy, it should be standardised, *e.g.*, against pure silver nitrite.

Aluminium hydroxide suspension—Dissolve 125 g of aluminium potassium sulphate, $Al_2(SO_4)_3.K_2SO_4.24H_2O$, in about 1 litre of distilled water. Precipitate the aluminium hydroxide by adding ammonium hydroxide slowly in slight excess, with stirring. Allow the precipitate to settle, then wash it by decantation with distilled water until it is free from chloride, nitrate, nitrite and ammonia. Finally, dilute the suspension to 1 litre with distilled water.

Activated charcoal, acid-washed.

PROCEDURE—

If the effluent sample requires preliminary clarification or decolorisation, proceed as follows—

Add approximately 0·5 g of activated charcoal to 100 ml of the sample and shake the mixture; then add 1 ml of aluminium hydroxide suspension, shake again and, after allowing the mixture to settle, filter it through a close-textured filter-paper, rejecting the first 20 ml of filtrate.

Into a series of matched 50-ml Nessler cylinders, measure volumes between 0 and 2·0 ml of dilute standard nitrite solution B. Into another matched Nessler cylinder measure a suitable quantity of the sample, or of the filtrate resulting from the preliminary treatment described above.

Fill the cylinders to the 50-ml mark with distilled water. To each add 1 ml of sulphanilic acid solution and, after an interval of 5 minutes, 1 ml of 1-naphthylamine solution. Allow the cylinders to stand for 15 minutes in diffused light. Compare the colour produced by the sample with that of the standards.

If x ml of the sample are equivalent to y ml of dilute standard nitrite solution B, then—

$$\text{Nitrite nitrogen (mg per litre)} = \frac{0·5\,y}{x}.$$

The colour produced may also be matched with standard glass discs that can be purchased. Alternatively, the optical density may be measured in a spectrophotometer or in an absorptiometer, using a wavelength of 5461 A in the former or a suitable blue-green filter in the latter. The observed optical density is related to the number of milligrams of nitrite nitrogen by means of a previously prepared calibration graph.

When standard glass discs are used, the instructions of the manufacturers must be exactly followed. When an instrumental technique is used, rigid control of colour development and of temperature (around 20° C) is necessary.

INTERFERENCE OF CHLORIDE—

It has been stated that the presence of chloride influences the results obtained in this test. According to Klein,[6] however, chloride concentrations of less than 500 mg per litre have no appreciable effect. When it is considered that there is interference by chloride, its effect may be "drowned" by adding 1 ml of saturated sodium chloride solution to both sample and standards.

NITROGEN PRESENT AS NITRATE

Effluents containing oxidised nitrogen products usually contain both nitrite and nitrate. The former, however, is often present in only very small quantities, and in low concentration can be determined with considerable accuracy. Hence it is often practicable to arrive at a reliable figure for the nitrate concentration by determining the total oxidised nitrogen and subtracting the figure determined for nitrite.

PRINCIPLE OF METHOD—

Several methods are available for the determination of the total oxidised nitrogen. In general, these depend on reduction of the oxidised nitrogen to ammonia and subsequent determination of the ammonia contained in the solution by the methods described for the determination of ammoniacal nitrogen.

This method[7] may conveniently follow a determination of ammoniacal nitrogen involving distillation with light magnesium oxide. The oxidised compounds of nitrogen in the residue are then quantitatively reduced to ammonia on boiling with Devarda's alloy and the ammonia so produced is determined by distillation and titration or, if the content of nitrite plus nitrate is expected to be less than 4 mg of nitrogen per litre, by distillation and nesslerisation. The nitrate figure is found by deducting from the result of the determination of oxidised nitrogen the figure determined for nitrite. Evidence has been produced to show that this method gives satisfactory results irrespective of the amount of nitrite present.

REAGENTS—

In addition to the reagents listed under "Ammoniacal Nitrogen," the following is required.

Devarda's alloy, powdered—This must be as free from nitrogen as possible and fine enough to pass through a 200-mesh sieve.

PROCEDURE—

To the cooled residue in the flask after distillation of the ammoniacal nitrogen from 0·25 g of light magnesium oxide, as specified in the distillation and titration method under "Ammoniacal Nitrogen," add 1 g of powdered Devarda's alloy and sufficient ammonia-free distilled water to bring the volume in the flask to about 350 ml.

If more than 4 mg of nitrate nitrogen per litre are expected to be present, collect the ammonia in 50·0 ml of 0·01 N sulphuric acid and proceed as described under "Ammoniacal Nitrogen (titration method)."

If less than 4 mg per litre are present, proceed as described under "Ammoniacal Nitrogen (nesslerisation method)."

Heat the distilling flask carefully, reducing the flame when bubbles of gas become visible in order to avoid frothing and excessive spray formation as boiling begins. Boil gently for 5 to 10 minutes and then more vigorously, provided this does not cause excessive frothing. Continue the distillation until at least 150 ml of distillate have been collected. Carry out a blank determination by the method, using all the reagents.

Express the result as milligrams of nitrate nitrogen per litre of sample.

REFERENCES

1. Jenkins, S. H., *J. Inst. Sewage Purif.*, 1950, II, 144.
2. ——, *Ibid.*, 1950, II, 147.
3. Elek, A., and Sobotka, H., *J. Amer. Chem. Soc.*, 1926, **48**, 501.
4. Shirley, R. L., and Becker, W. W., *Ind. Eng. Chem., Anal. Ed.*, 1945, **17**, 437.
5. Friedrich, A., *Z. phys. Chem.*, 1933, **216**, 68.
6. Klein, L., *J. Inst. Sewage Purif.*, 1950, II, 153.
7. Jenkins, S. H., *Ibid.*, 1950, II, 145.

Phenols

The term "phenols" as used in this connection covers the monohydroxy derivatives of benzene and its homologues. These compounds are used in industry in the pure state and as mixtures, and the composition of the mixture of phenols present in an effluent is unpredictable. Different phenols give slightly differing colours with analytical reagents, but the first method ("Indophenol Method") gives satisfactory results for low concentrations. For higher concentrations, a titration method ("Bromination Method") is given.   In both methods the result is expressed as phenol, C_6H_5OH.

The determination should be made as soon as possible after the sample has been collected, since the phenol content tends to diminish, especially at low concentrations and at high temperatures.   If delay in the analysis is unavoidable, the phenols may be "fixed" by the addition of a small amount of sodium hydroxide solution to a portion of the sample reserved for the determination.

PRELIMINARY TREATMENT OF SAMPLE

Unless interfering substances (see under the relevant "Method") are known to be absent, the following preliminary treatment should be employed.   It should also be used if the sample is coloured.

REAGENTS—

Ammonium polysulphide solution—Dissolve a sufficient amount of sublimed sulphur in a solution of ammonium sulphide to produce a deep-yellow solution.
Sodium hydroxide solution, 10 *per cent. w/v.*
Sulphuric acid, dilute, 25 *per cent. w/v.*
Lead carbonate.

PROCEDURE—

Treat an appropriate volume of the sample (for the amount, see the relevant "Procedure") with a few drops of ammonium polysulphide solution to convert any cyanide present to thiocyanate, and allow the mixture to stand for about 10 minutes. Omit this treatment if cyanides are known to be absent.   Remove sulphide by the careful addition of a small excess of lead carbonate and filter the sample into a distillation flask.   Wash the filter-paper and precipitate with a small volume of distilled water, collecting the washings in the flask.   Add 10 ml of sodium hydroxide solution and connect the flask to a water-cooled condenser.   Boil the contents of the flask and distil and reject a volume of distillate equal to 20 per cent. of that in the flask.   (This treatment removes amines.)   Cool the flask and add to it 10 ml of dilute sulphuric acid.   Distil and collect a volume of distillate equal to the original volume of the sample.   A small volume of water may be added to the contents of the flask if necessary to enable this to be done.   Examine the distillate by one of the methods given below, according to the amount of phenol expected.

INDOPHENOL METHOD
PRINCIPLE OF METHOD—

"Phenols" react with *p*-aminodimethylaniline in the presence of a mild oxidising agent to give a blue colour, which is measured or compared with standards.

RANGE—

The method is directly applicable to solutions containing 0·1 to 1 mg of phenols per litre.   Stronger solutions may be diluted with water before being tested; weaker solutions are dealt with by a slight modification.

APPLICABILITY—

The method is directly applicable to a wide variety of solutions, but amines must be absent in the actual solution tested.   (See "Preliminary Treatment of Sample.")

REAGENTS—

Carbon tetrachloride.

Sodium bicarbonate solution, 5 per cent. w/v.

Potassium ferricyanide solution, 8 per cent. w/v.

Standard phenol solution, 0·001 per cent. w/v—Prepare immediately before use by diluting 1 ml of a 0·1 per cent. w/v aqueous solution of pure phenol to 100 ml with distilled water.

p-*Aminodimethylaniline reagent*—Since the purchased base, its dihydrochloride and sulphate are unstable* and tend to discolour on being kept, the following method of preparation is recommended—

> Prepare a 0·1 per cent. w/v solution of p-nitrosodimethylaniline by dissolving the pure crystalline compound in water near its boiling-point. Reduce the solution with a large excess of zinc dust and a small amount of sodium bicarbonate solution (about 8 g of zinc and 2 ml of sodium bicarbonate solution per 25 ml of solution). The reduction proceeds better if the solution is warm. If difficulty is experienced, 1 drop of 10 per cent. w/v copper sulphate solution may be added. The reduced solution should be colourless. Cool and filter the solution.

PROCEDURE—

The solution for test will normally be the distillate from the preliminary treatment of the sample. A sample volume of 100 ml is convenient for distillation, unless the concentration of phenol is very low (see Note). The phenol content of the solution under test should be adjusted by dilution if necessary to lie between 0·1 and 1·0 mg per litre.

Measure 50 ml of the solution for test into a separating funnel and add 2 ml of sodium bicarbonate solution together with 2 ml of p-aminodimethylaniline reagent. Then add 2 ml of potassium ferricyanide solution and mix well. A blue colour will slowly develop. After 15 minutes extract the coloured solution with two successive 20-ml amounts of carbon tetrachloride. Dry the combined extracts with a small amount of anhydrous sodium sulphate and filter the mixture, washing the filter-paper with a small volume of solvent, and dilute the filtrate to 50·0 ml.

Simultaneously, using the same procedure, prepare from the standard phenol solution a series of standard solutions covering the range 0·1 to 1·0 mg of phenol.

Determine the phenol content of the sample either by visual colour comparison with the standards or instrumentally, by means of a spectrophotometer or an absorptiometer.

If an instrument is employed, use a wavelength of 6000 to 6100 A in a spectrophotometer or a suitable red filter in an absorptiometer, and read the phenol content equivalent to the observed optical density from a previously prepared calibration graph; this is established by relating the optical densities of the standards to their phenol content. Express the results as milligrams of phenol per litre of sample.

> NOTE—For samples of very low phenol content, a larger sample volume may be treated and finally extracted with the same volume (50 ml in all) of solvent as above, appropriate adjustments being made in the volumes of other reagents and in calculating the result.

BROMINATION METHOD

PRINCIPLE OF METHOD—

The phenols in the sample are brominated with a standard solution of potassium bromate and bromide, and the excess of bromine is determined by titration.

---

* The oxalate of p-aminodimethylaniline, which is also available commercially, is sufficiently stable to be used for the preparation of the reagent solution.

RANGE—

For samples containing more than 20 mg of phenols per litre of sample.

APPLICABILITY—

Substances, other than phenols, that react with bromine, *e.g.*, reducing agents and unsaturated organic compounds, will interfere with the method. The preliminary treatment described above should satisfactorily eliminate most of the substances likely to interfere.

REAGENTS—

Bromate - bromide solution, 0·5 N—Dissolve 13·92 g of potassium bromate and 75 g of potassium bromide in sufficient distilled water to produce 1 litre.
Sulphuric acid, dilute, 25 per cent. w/v.
Potassium iodide solution, 10 per cent. w/v.
Sodium thiosulphate solution, 0·2 N.
Carbon tetrachloride.
Starch indicator solution.

PROCEDURE—

For samples containing between 20 and 200 mg of phenol per litre, take 200 ml of the sample.

For samples containing between 200 and 500 mg per litre take 100 ml of the sample. For stronger solutions, take such a volume as contains from 0·02 to 0·05 g of phenol and dilute to 100 ml with distilled water.

Transfer the sample under test, which will usually be the distillate from the "Preliminary Treatment of Sample", to an iodine flask and add 20·0 ml of bromate - bromide solution from a pipette; then add 10 ml of dilute sulphuric acid. Quickly re-insert the stopper and seal the neck of the flask with 10 ml of potassium iodide solution. Allow the flask to stand for 1 hour in the dark at room temperature, and then wash the sealing solution into the flask and add a further 10 ml of potassium iodide solution. Titrate the liberated iodine with 0·2 N sodium thiosulphate solution, adding a few drops of starch indicator solution and a few drops of carbon tetrachloride near the end-point. Standardise the thiosulphate soluion against the bromate - bromide solution, using the same procedure.

Find, by difference, the volume of bromate - bromide solution used in brominating the phenol.

1 ml of 0·5 N bromide - bromate solution ≡ 0·0078 g of phenol.

Express the result as milligrams of phenol per litre of sample.

Phosphorus

PRINCIPLE OF METHOD—

Phosphorus may be present in effluents as phosphate (ortho-, meta-, pyro- or polyphosphate) and in organic combination.

The phosphorus is first converted to orthophosphate, if not already present as such. This is then determined colorimetrically (by using Tschopps's reagent) as the molybdenum blue complex formed by the reduction of molybdophosphoric acid.

RANGE—

For phosphorus contents of (*a*) up to 75 μg (instrumental method)
or (*b*) up to 25 μg (visual colour-comparison method).

APPLICABILITY—

The method is of wide applicability.   Ferric iron in concentrations several times that of the phosphorus does not interfere.

The conditions of test may be modified to differentiate between total inorganic phosphate and total phosphorus present in the effluent.

NOTE—It is possible that extraction procedures[1,2] may be of assistance in eliminating interferences.   In these procedures the molybdophosphoric acid is extracted by a solvent such as n-butanol, and the reduction is subsequently carried out in this medium.

REAGENTS—

Ammonium molybdate solution—Dissolve 10 g of ammonium molybdate, $(NH_4)_6Mo_7O_{24}.4H_2O$, in 100 ml of distilled water.   Add this solution slowly, and with stirring, to 300 ml of diluted sulphuric acid $(1 + 1)$.   Store in a borosilicate-glass bottle in the dark.

Standard phosphate solution A—Dissolve 0·439 g of potassium dihydrogen orthophosphate in distilled water, add 5 ml of diluted sulphuric acid $(1 + 1)$ and dilute the solution to 1 litre.

Standard phosphate solution B—Dilute 10·0 ml of solution A to 1 litre with distilled water.   Prepare this solution freshly each day.

$$1 \text{ ml} \equiv 1 \text{ } \mu g \text{ of phosphorus.}$$

Metol - sulphite solution (Tschopps's reagent)—Dissolve 40 g of sodium metabisulphite and 1 g of sodium sulphite, $Na_2SO_3.7H_2O$, in cold distilled water, add 0·2 g of Metol (p-methylaminophenol sulphate) and stir well until solution is complete. Dilute to 100 ml with distilled water and mix.

PROCEDURE—

(a)   Total inorganic phosphate

Select a suitable volume of the effluent sample (not exceeding 10 ml) to contain up to 75 μg of phosphorus if the determination is to be made instrumentally, or up to 25 μg if visual colour comparison is to be made.

Add sufficient sulphuric acid to make the acidity 5 N and boil the solution for 15 minutes, to convert any condensed phosphates to orthophosphate, keeping the volume constant.   Cool, filter, if necessary, and almost neutralise to phenolphthalein with sodium hydroxide solution.

Add 5 ml of ammonium molybdate solution and 5 ml of Metol - sulphite solution. Heat the solution in a boiling-water bath for 30 minutes and then cool to room temperature.   Transfer the solution to a 50-ml calibrated flask and dilute to the mark with distilled water.

Carry out a blank procedure on all reagents used.   Proceed to determine the phosphorus content colorimetrically, either by the instrumental method or by visual colour comparison.

Instrumental method—Measure the optical densities of the test and blank solutions in a spectrophotometer or in an absorptiometer, using 4-cm or 1-cm cells according to the depth of colour, and using a wavelength of 6500 A in a spectrophotometer or a suitable red filter in an absorptiometer.   Use distilled water in the comparison cell.   Read the number of micrograms of phosphorus equivalent to the observed optical densities of the test and blank solutions from a previously prepared calibration graph, and so obtain the net measure of inorganic phosphate (as phosphorus) in the sample.

Express the total inorganic phosphate content as milligrams of phosphorus per litre of sample.

Establish the calibration graph as follows—

Measure appropriate amounts of standard phosphate solution B into a series of conical flasks: for the 4-cm cell the standards should cover the range 0 to 10 μg and for the 1-cm cell they should cover the range 10 to 75 μg of phosphorus. To the contents of each flask add 5 ml of ammonium molybdate solution and 5 ml of Metol - sulphite solution and proceed as for the test sample. Measure the optical densities and construct a graph relating the optical densities to the number of micrograms of phosphorus.

Visual colour-comparison method—Prepare a series of standards as for the instrumental method, covering the range 0 to 25 μg of phosphorus. Compare the colours visually in Nessler cylinders.

Alternatively, proprietary coloured discs may be used in a comparator instead of solution standards, and the makers' instructions should be followed. It should be noted that some proprietary coloured discs are calibrated in terms of P_2O_5; the conversion factor to phosphorus is 0·437.

(b) Total phosphorus

Digest 5 to 10 ml of the effluent sample, over a micro-burner, with 0·3 to 0·5 ml of sulphuric acid, sp.gr. 1·84, in a micro-Kjeldahl flask or boiling-tube. Continue the digestion until the solution is colourless, avoiding loss by fuming. Cool and transfer the solution to a 50-ml calibrated flask, rinsing the digestion vessel with sufficient distilled water to bring the volume to about 20 ml; filter if necessary. Almost neutralise the solution to phenolphthalein with sodium hydroxide solution. Finally, dilute the solution to the mark with distilled water.

Measure a suitable aliquot of this solution and proceed as described under "Total Inorganic Phosphate," commencing at "Add 5 ml of ammonium molybdate solution . . . " in (a) above.

Carry out a blank determination on all reagents used.

Express the total phosphorus content as milligrams of phosphorus per litre of sample.

REFERENCES

1. Pons, W. A., and Guthrie, J. D., *Ind. Eng. Chem., Anal. Ed.*, 1946, **18**, 184.
2. Martin, J. B., and Doty, D. M., *Anal. Chem.*, 1949, **21**, 965.

Combined Sulphur

ACID-SOLUBLE SULPHATE

PRINCIPLE OF METHOD—

The acid-soluble sulphates are precipitated as barium sulphate under controlled conditions[1] and determined gravimetrically.

RANGE—

For sulphate contents between 8 and 60 mg, expressed as SO_4''.

APPLICABILITY—

The method is generally applicable. If it is desired to include the sulphate ion of insoluble compounds, such as barium sulphate, an appropriate aliquot of the well-mixed sample must be neutralised, made slightly acid with hydrochloric acid, evaporated to dryness, ignited and the usual methods of quantitative gravimetric analysis applied to the residue.

REAGENTS—

Hydrochloric acid, sp.gr. 1·18.

Hydrochloric acid, diluted (1 + 1).

Hydrochloric acid, dilute, approximately 0·5 N.

Ammonium hydroxide, diluted (1 + 3)—Dilute 1 volume of ammonium hydroxide, sp.gr. 0·880, with 3 volumes of distilled water.

Barium chloride solution, 10 *per cent. w/v.*

Methyl orange indicator solution—A 0·04 per cent. w/v solution in 20 per cent. ethanol.

PROCEDURE—

Measure an aliquot of the effluent sample which is expected to contain between 8 and 60 mg of acid-soluble sulphate. Neutralise with 0·5 N hydrochloric acid, using methyl orange indicator solution; then add 1 ml of hydrochloric acid, sp.gr. 1·18, and boil the mixture. Adjust the volume to about 150 ml by concentration or dilution with distilled water. Filter the solution and wash the residue on the filter-paper until the washings are free from chloride.

Neutralise the combined filtrate and washings with diluted ammonium hydroxide (1 + 3), adding more indicator solution if necessary. Adjust the volume to about 200 ml with distilled water, add 2 ml of diluted hydrochloric acid (1 + 1) and heat to boiling. Boil the solution for about 30 seconds, remove it from the hot-plate and add 10 ml of barium chloride solution (or 15 ml if less than 20 mg of sulphate are present) from a fast-flowing pipette to the centre of the solution, with thorough mixing. Allow the mixture to stand for 20 minutes; then filter off the precipitate on an ashless filter-paper pulp pad, using gravity filtration and washing with hot distilled water until the washings are free from chloride.

Transfer the wet pad and precipitate to a previously ignited and weighed silica capsule, wiping off with a piece of moist filter-paper any precipitate adhering to the funnel, insert the capsule on a 6-mm silica plate directly into a well-ventilated muffle furnace at 800° C, ignite, cool and weigh the barium sulphate.

Weight of $BaSO_4$ (in mg) $\times$ 0·4116 = mg of sulphate (as SO_4'').

Express the result as milligrams of acid-soluble sulphate (as SO_4'') per litre of sample.

SULPHIDE

INTRODUCTION—

The method described below is for the determination of the total sulphide present. The determination of sulphide should be made with the minimum of delay after the taking of the sample to avoid oxidation and loss of free hydrogen sulphide.

If an immediate analysis is not possible, the hydrogen sulphide must be "fixed" by precipitation of the sulphide with zinc acetate as described under "Procedure."

PRINCIPLE OF METHOD—

After acidification the free and combined hydrogen sulphide is displaced from the sample by a stream of inert gas and absorbed in a solution of zinc acetate. The hydrogen sulphide is again liberated from the zinc sulphide and oxidised with an excess of iodine. The amount of iodine used is determined by titration.

RANGE—

The method is given for concentrations above 5 mg of sulphide per litre of sample and a variation is given for concentrations below 5 mg per litre.

APPLICABILITY—

The method is generally applicable, but volatile compounds that react with iodine, and those substances that produce such compounds on acidification, e.g., thiosulphate, necessitate a preliminary "fixing" (see first paragraph under "Procedure").

APPARATUS—

A wide-mouthed bottle or flask having a capacity of about 1 litre. The cork carries a small dropping funnel, an inlet tube and an outlet tube. The inlet tube has a sintered-glass diffuser on the end.

Two small conical flasks fitted with corks and inlet and outlet tubes to constitute two absorbing flasks in series.

REAGENTS—

Hydrochloric acid, diluted (1 + 1).

Zinc acetate solution, 25 per cent. w/v.

Dilute zinc acetate solution, 2 per cent. w/v—Prepare this solution freshly as required.

Sodium thiosulphate solution, 0·1 N and 0·01 N.*

Iodine solution, 0·1 N and 0·01 N.*

Starch indicator solution.

PROCEDURE—

If the presence of interfering substances is suspected, or if the analysis has to be delayed, add 25 per cent. zinc acetate solution to a measured volume of sample in the proportion of 2 ml per litre, respectively. Allow the precipitate to settle. Decant the clear supernatant liquor through a small filter-paper; then transfer the precipitate to the paper. If sulphite and thiosulphate are to be determined retain the precipitate. Transfer the filter-paper and precipitate to the wide-mouthed bottle or flask with 500 ml of distilled water. Proceed as described below, starting at "Connect the outlet tube of the bottle. . . ."

If the analysis is to be made immediately after sampling, and no interfering substances are present, measure 500 ml of the effluent sample (or a suitable aliquot if the sulphide content is known to be high) into the wide-necked bottle or flask.

Connect the outlet tube of the bottle or flask to the two conical flasks arranged in series as absorbers. If a smaller volume of sample is taken, add distilled water to make the volume up to about 500 ml. In each absorption vessel place 50 ml of 2 per cent. zinc acetate solution. Connect the delivery tube and diffuser to a source of carbon dioxide, nitrogen or other inert gas, free from oxygen. Measure 50 ml of diluted hydrochloric acid (1 + 1) into the dropping funnel and add it slowly to the sample, maintaining a slow steady stream of inert gas through the system.

The hydrogen sulphide will be carried forward and precipitated as zinc sulphide in the absorption flasks. Continue the passage of the gas for 1 hour; then disconnect the absorbers. Add to each absorber a measured volume of 0·1 N iodine solution (or 0·01 N if the sulphide content of the sample is less than 5 mg per litre) so that a small excess is present. The second flask will require a much smaller volume of iodine solution than the first. To each add 10 ml of diluted hydrochloric acid, allow the solution to stand for 10 minutes and titrate the excess of iodine with 0·1 N (or 0·01 N) thiosulphate solution, using starch indicator solution.

* The 0·01 N solutions do not keep and should be freshly prepared.

A blank test should be carried out using the same volumes of reagent, but omitting the sample under test.

Calculate the *total* net volume of 0·1 *N* (or 0·01 *N*) iodine solution used by subtracting the *total* volume of 0·1 *N* (or 0·01 *N*) sodium thiosulphate solution.

1 ml of 0·1 N iodine solution ≡ 0·0017 g of hydrogen sulphide.

Express the result as milligrams of hydrogen sulphide per litre of sample.

SULPHITE AND THIOSULPHATE

PRINCIPLE OF METHOD—

In this method,[2] the total iodine equivalent of sulphite and thiosulphate is determined; on a separate portion sulphite is masked by formaldehyde and the iodine equivalent of the thiosulphate is determined.

RANGE—

For sulphite contents (as SO_3'') greater than 2 mg per litre of sample, and for thiosulphate contents (as S_2O_3'') greater than 5 mg per litre of sample.

APPLICABILITY—

The method is generally applicable. Sulphide interferes and, if present, is first removed as zinc sulphide.

REAGENTS—

Hydrochloric acid, sp.gr. 1·18.
Acetic acid, glacial.
Zinc acetate solution, 25 per cent. *w/v.*
or
Zinc carbonate, finely divided.
Formaldehyde solution, 40 per cent. *w/v.*
Potassium iodide solution, 10 per cent. *w/v.*
Iodine solution, 0·01 N—Prepare this solution freshly as required.
Sodium thiosulphate solution, 0·01 N—Prepare this solution freshly as required.
Starch indicator solution.

PROCEDURE—

Sulphite and thiosulphate—If sulphide is present in the effluent sample, add sufficient zinc acetate solution to precipiate the sulphide and filter off the zinc sulphide. Alternatively, shake the sample with an excess of finely divided zinc carbonate, allow the precipitate to settle and then filter. If sulphide is to be determined, retain the precipitate.

Measure 200 ml of the filtrate (or of the effluent sample if sulphide is known to be absent) into a 500-ml flask containing 25·0 ml of 0·01 *N* iodine solution and 2 ml of hydrochloric acid, pouring the sample carefully down the side of the flask and mixing gently. Titrate the excess of iodine with 0·01 *N* sodium thiosulphate solution, adding the starch indicator solution near the end-point.

Thiosulphate alone—To a further 200 ml of effluent sample or filtrate add 5 ml of formaldehyde solution, and then 2 ml of acetic acid and 2 ml of potassium iodide solution. Titrate with 0·01 *N* iodine solution, using starch indicator solution.

The difference between the two values for the iodine equivalents gives that of the sulphite.

1 ml of 0·01 N iodine solution ≡ 0·4 mg of sulphite (as SO_3''), or
≡ 0·56 mg of thiosulphate (as S_2O_3'').

Express the results as milligrams of sulphite or thiosulphate per litre of sample.

REFERENCES

1. Mott, R. A., Ruell, D. A., and Wilkinson, H. C., *Fuel*, 1955, **34**, 78 and 87.
2. Fogg, D. N., and Wilkinson, N. T., *J. Appl. Chem.*, 1952, **2**, 357.

APPENDIX

Flame Photometry

ANY flame photometer can be considered as consisting of three units, the source, the analyser and the detector. There are many possible variations in the way an instrument is made, and its versatility will depend on several factors.

In the source unit a sample is atomised and the fine spray so produced is introduced into a flame. The method of atomising is not important in this consideration, but the temperature of the flame determines the range of elements that are suitably excited. If, for instance, an air - propane mixture is used, usually alkalis and perhaps alkaline earths are easily excited. If an oxygen - acetylene mixture is used, a large number of elements are excited, including Na, K, Rb, Cs, Li, Ca, Sr, Ba, Cu, Co, Ni, Ag, Mn, Mg, Fe and B.

The analyser unit may be a monochromator or a filter. This may be an interference filter or a coloured filter of the usual type or a solution, or any combination of these. The function of the analyser is to isolate from the total flame output the required wavelengths, and the efficiency with which this is done will be a function of the band-width transmitted at any one setting by the analyser. A monochromator is much more efficient for this purpose than are filters and can be set to transmit any desired wavelength.

The detector unit consists of a photocell or photomultiplier whose output is read on a sensitive galvanometer or on a suitable meter after amplification.

In any analysis by flame photometry it is necessary to relate the method to the particular instrument used. If, for instance, the equipment comprises a hot flame (air - acetylene, oxy-hydrogen or oxy-acetylene), good monochromator and sensitive detector, then probably it is necessary only to dilute the sample suitably and to take readings on an instrument calibrated against standard solutions.

If the flame photometer consists of a cool flame (air - propane or air - coal gas) and optical filters, there are two points to consider. Firstly, only the alkalis and alkaline earths are easily excited and anionic interference is likely to be very serious in the determination of the latter; if, for example, the sample contains any phosphate, the possibility of determining calcium is virtually eliminated. Secondly, filters may not efficiently isolate the required monochromatic radiation from the total emission of the flame, and in that case corrections may be required or some other means may have to be employed to eliminate the interfering element or elements.

In view of these considerations the following recommendations are made.

Potassium—In the absence of barium, rubidium or caesium it is necessary only to dilute the sample suitably to be able to determine potassium on any type of instrument. If these are present, a monochromator instrument is required.

Sodium—Calcium is likely to be the main interfering element. If it is absent, or if it is present in amounts that do not interfere (this can only be determined by experiment), then simple dilution of the sample is the only preparation required.

If a monochromator instrument is used, fairly large excesses of calcium can be tolerated; for example, on one such instrument, if a solution containing, say, 1 to 5 p.p.m. of sodium is being assayed, calcium causes no interference in concentrations up to 1000 p.p.m.

If a filter instrument is used, calcium will interfere at low concentrations because it will emit some light.   If the calcium concentration is known accurately, it may be possible to apply suitable corrections, but perhaps the better approach is to precipitate it as calcium oxalate and remove it by filtration.

Other elements that could interfere are barium and boron; the latter would need to be present in high concentration and only the hotter flames would excite it.

Calcium—Calcium can be determined satisfactorily by using a hot flame and a monochromator instrument.   If phosphate is present it will interfere by depressing the intensity of the emission and its effect may be compensated for by adding an excess of phosphate both to standards and sample, or it can be removed by using an anion-exchange resin.   Aluminium produces a similar depressive effect that can be obviated by adding an excess of strontium both to standards and sample. Sodium in excess will interfere, but its effect can be minimised by using a Chance ON16 (or similar) filter between the flame and the monochromator.

In a cool flame the calcium emission is affected seriously by changes in anionic type and concentration, and by phosphate in particular.   A cool flame can therefore only be used for the simplest of samples.   Interference by sodium is more serious in a filter instrument than in one using a monochromator.

Other elements—The elements that can be determined depend entirely on the instrument.   If it comprises a monochromator and a very sensitive detector, it will be possible to determine any element excited in the flame.   It is generally true that as the flame temperature increases more elements will be excited and sensitivity will improve.   The bottom limit of sensitivity will vary from element to element and with the conditions.   It is obvious that smaller amounts can be determined after concentration of the sample.

Selected Bibliography

Mavrodineanu, R., (Part I*), *Applied Spectroscopy*, 1956, **10**, 51.
Mavrodineanu, R., (Part II*), *Ibid.*, 1956, **10**, 137.
Marsh, G. E., *Ibid.*, 1956, **10**, 8.
Collins, G. C., and Polkinhorne, H., *Analyst*, 1952, **77**, 430.
Holiday, E. R., and Preedy, J. R. K., *Biochem. J.*, 1953, **55**, 214.

* These two papers together comprise a complete bibliography on the subject.

Index